Where The Dead Fall

# MJ LEE
# WHERE THE DEAD FALL

CANELO

First published in the United Kingdom in 2019 by Canelo

This edition published in the United Kingdom in 2019 by

Canelo Digital Publishing Limited
57 Shepherds Lane
Beaconsfield, Bucks HP9 2DU
United Kingdom

A CIP catalogue record for this book is available from the British Library.

Print ISBN 978 1 78863 574 5
Ebook ISBN 978 1 78863 317 8

This book is a work of fiction. Names, characters, businesses, organizations, places and events are either the product of the author's imagination or are used fictitiously. Any resemblance to actual persons, living or dead, events or locales is entirely coincidental.

Look for more great books at www.canelo.co

Printed and bound in Great Britain by Clays Ltd, Elcograf S.p.A.

*For Jimmy Hewitt 1921 – 1992.*
*A true Salford Lad.*
*Ex-Red Beret, lover of Guinness and Salford Red Devils,*
*who never saw a doctor for forty-three years.*
*This book is dedicated to you, Jimmy.*

## Two Days Earlier

*How long had he been here?*

*Hours?*

*Days?*

He didn't know. There were no windows to give him any sense of passing time, just a bright neon light beaming through the fanlight above the door.

He turned his head and licked the slime-covered wall, tasting the rancid wet mould on his tongue as he searched for moisture.

*Why was he so thirsty?*

He licked again, hoping against hope a few drops of precious liquid would coat his tongue and moisten his cracked lips.

Nothing.

Just the taste of damp, rotten mushrooms.

*How long had he been here?*

He shifted position once again, the ropes around his wrists chafing against his skin. As he did, he kicked the plastic water bottle lying at his feet, sending it crashing against the far wall where it spun for a few seconds before coming to rest in front of the door. It was empty anyway, the contents drunk long ago.

He should have saved some, not guzzled it all.

Why was he so thirsty?

He shook his head.

*Think. Think clearly.*

An Uber to her house, leaving his Merc in the city.

Better she said. You've had too much to drink, she said.

When had that ever stopped him before?

In her house, the one her father had left her, she said.

Drinking. Drinking what? Vodka and Red Bull. Feeling drowsy. Waking up alone on the floor. Naked, except for a pair of blue boxers.

*What was going on?*

Screaming. Yelling. Pounding on the door.

Again. And again. And again.

Nobody came. Nobody heard. The room seemed to absorb all his noise but gave nothing back in return.

Screaming again and again and again. His voice hoarse, his mouth dry. But still nobody came.

Then, he had stopped, taken a few deep breaths, calmed himself.

*Why was he here?*

He had done nothing wrong to her. Never.

He listened for any noise: the sound of traffic, the wind rustling through the leaves of a tree, the tread of a foot on a step.

Nothing.

Cold. Hugging himself to keep warm. Bare arms tied at the wrists, hooked over bare legs.

He would kill her when he saw her again. Enjoy every second as she squealed in pain and terror.

Then walking. Three strides and a half across one way, four strides the other.

Up and down. Up and down.

It was a box.

His box.

He had tried biting through the rope holding his wrists together but it wasn't long before the fibres had cut his gums, the blood tasting metallic in his mouth.

He had banged on the metal door again till his hands bled but still nobody came.

*Was he going to die here alone? What had he done to deserve this?*

And then he started crying, snivelling as salty tears ran down his cheeks. His father's voice from long ago in his head, cajoling, threatening. 'No son of mine is going to bow down to nobody. Now go back and give that bully a kicking. Make sure you hurt him real bad.'

So he had gone back to school, walked up to the bully during playtime and hit him over the head with a cricket bat stolen from the gym.

The boy toppled like a tree, cut down in its prime.

Toppled and lay there, unmoving.

He got expelled the next day but his dad was proud of him. That was all that mattered, making his dad proud.

He met the bully at the shops a week later. The boy crossed the street to avoid him.

A good memory. Making his dad proud.

He chewed the rope once more despite the pain, twisting his mouth so his canine teeth came in contact with it.

He would escape, he wasn't going to be trapped here for the rest of his life. Soon, the family would realise he was missing. His father would come looking for him, wouldn't he?

His mouth was dry, all spit absorbed by the rope. He stared at his wrists. A few fibres were sticking out from the rope but otherwise it looked untouched.

*Why was he so thirsty?*

He stared at the slime-covered wall in the light from above the door. Could he lick it again? Anything for a few drops of water to moisten his dry mouth.

He was about to lean forward when the green slime darkened, vanishing from view.

What?

What was happening? Were they going to let him go?

A shadow covered the door. The handle was turning, the click of a key in the lock. The smell of cigarette smoke filling the room.

A man framed in the door, silhouetted by the neon light.

'It's time we had some fun.'

# Day One

*Wednesday, April 18, 2018*

# Chapter One

Detective Inspector Thomas Ridpath had a broad smile on his face.

It wasn't that he had successfully negotiated the tangle of roads, side roads and unintelligible signage on the transition from the M62 to the M60 ring road around Manchester.

It wasn't that he had just come top in his residential course for coroners' officers. The course itself was easy; ten years as a copper on the mean streets of Manchester ensured he could handle a few questions thrown at him by a bunch of pasty-white academics.

It wasn't even that he had received the latest all-clear from Christies Hospital whilst on the course; his myeloma was still in remission. Each month he dreaded the phone call from the doctor. It was like waiting for the axe to fall as he knelt with his head on the block. This month he had another stay of execution. The axeman remained standing above him though, his axe frozen at the peak of its arc.

He had to go back for another check-up on Friday. More cigarettes as the tension built before his appointment. More blood to feed the nurse he had come to know as the Vampire. More trembling hands as he waited to see the doctor. Then the nurse calling his name and the long, awkward 5 yard trek to the doctor's room. Knocking on the door, waiting for the word 'Enter'. The terrible emptiness of anticipation as the doctor examined his results, clicking the buttons of his old NHS desktop and then turning to him to say...

Ridpath banished the image from his mind.

Think positive thoughts.

He smiled broadly again.

Tonight was going to be a good night. After two weeks away he would finally be able to see Polly and Eve, his wife and daughter. Not that Polly was too chuffed to see him at the moment; he had blotted his copybook badly during the Beast of Manchester case. She had walked out of the home, taking their daughter with her.

At least they were talking to each other now and, with a bit of luck, he could persuade her to come home. He would have to find a face-saving formula to allow her to come back. A promise of better behaviour in the future should do it, but Polly had a streak of Chinese stubbornness a mile wide threading through her like 'Blackpool' through a stick of rock.

Tonight, though, she had agreed he could spend some time with his daughter, taking Eve to see the latest Disney movie.

He glanced down at the dashboard clock.

5:28 p.m.

The rush hour traffic was heavy as he drove over Barton Bridge but at least it was still flowing. There should be no problem with time. He'd promised to pick Eve up from Polly's parents' home on Princess Parkway at 6:30 p.m. He was just twenty minutes away at the most. Should be able to stop at the newsagents and pick up a paper and some fags.

He wasn't supposed to smoke; it was another area of contention between himself and Polly, but try as he might it was a vice he couldn't stop.

The doctors nagged him. Polly nagged him. Even Eve nagged him. He knew it was stupid, a triumph of pleasure over sense, but he smoked anyway. Sometimes it was better not to reason a need.

A car overtook him in the outside lane, a red and white scarf hanging out of the rear window. There must be a United game at Old Trafford tonight. A good job he had timed his return pretty well. An hour later and the road would be full of fans driving to the game.

6

The green dome of the Trafford Centre caught his eye on the left as it bathed in the light of the April sun. He hated the place with a passion; identikit shops selling the same identikit rubbish, restaurants producing mountains of overcooked stodge, a voluminous eating hall designed in the shape of the deck of an ocean liner and air that smelt like it had been filtered through the lungs of a thousand sweaty elephants.

If hell was a shopping mall, then the Trafford Centre was the dead centre. The fact that it was packed with whining Scousers on a day out from the prison known as Liverpool made it even worse. Only Scousers could think a good day out was a trip to hell.

The radio jingled with suitably urgent music. A brief news report: Brexit negotiations were going as badly as ever, Windrush was a terrible indictment on the Home Office and the President of the United States was tweeting insults again.

He pressed the control on his steering column, trying to find a different station. A station with music; a bit of soul, or even better, Bowie in his Ziggy Stardust incarnation, but all he could hear was a variety of newscasters droning on. He tried not to listen to the news any more. It depressed him even more than thinking about his cancer.

The traffic was speeding up as the Trafford Centre receded into the distance. The signage said Stretford, Sale and Altrincham on the left. Normally he would turn off here and head for home, but he carried straight on to the Dragon's Lair, aka Polly's mum, just two more junctions to the exit.

On the other side of the road traffic was already thickening as commuters headed home or headed north. Some of them may have been heading to the Lakes or Scotland. Perhaps he could take Eve walking in the Lakes for a weekend? Polly might even join them. She hated the idea of hiking though. 'What's the point of spending three hours huffing and puffing up a mountain only to come down two minutes later?' she had once told him with unerring Chinese–British logic.

She had gone with them anyway, enjoying the clean fresh air and reading Wordsworth's poetry from the comfort of the pub as he and Eve climbed Helvellyn.

Before he got ill.

Before the chemo.

Before they split up.

Around him, more cars raced past, with even more scarves hanging out of the windows. He didn't bother going to United any more. Since Sir Alex left the joy had gone out of the team for him. They were just another bunch of over-hyped, overpaid athletes who had somehow lost the spirit that was the football club.

Shame.

Up ahead he caught the flash of something white on the hard shoulder.

A naked man?

What was a naked man doing beside the motorway?

The white Ford in front of him on the inside lane honked a loud scream of disapproval.

The man looked right, towards the oncoming cars, but ran into the road anyway. Ridpath jammed his foot on the brake, pushing down as hard as he could, forcing his body into the seat.

The brakes screeched in anger.

The man was running across the road. The white car swerved left, its rear end fishtailing violently.

The man kept on running as the Ford missed him by inches.

Ridpath stamped on his brake harder. He glanced into his mirror, praying to God there wasn't another car close behind accelerating to smash into his rear.

The man continued running, all the time looking across at Ridpath getting ever closer, and then he stopped in the middle of the road, like a wild animal caught in the glare of the headlights.

Except it was broad daylight on the M60 in the middle of the rush hour.

For Ridpath the world slowed to a crawl. He gripped the steering wheel as the man turned slowly, getting bigger in the television that was the windscreen. Ridpath braced his body for impact. The man was facing him now, staring directly at the car racing towards him, his eyes large and his naked chest white.

What was on his chest?

A large pair of outstretched blue angel wings. Why would he have a pair of angel's wings on his chest?

The car squealed as the tyres dug into the grey tarmac leaving a trail of burnt rubber. Ridpath pressed harder with his foot, forcing it down into the floor, changing down to use the engine to slow the car.

The man was closer, closer.

Ridpath could see he was young with short black hair and an unshaven face, wearing nothing but a pair of blue boxer shorts and the angel wings covering his chest and white ribs.

He wasn't going to stop in time.

The rear end of the Vauxhall Vectra began to fishtail. He held onto the wheel even tighter. The man was right in front of him.

Nowhere to run now.

Ridpath closed his eyes, bracing himself for the impact, hearing the crunch of metal on bone, the body flying through the air, blood leaking from an open mouth.

As the screech of the brakes suddenly stopped, he was forced forward, gripped tightly across the chest by his seatbelt.

The car had stopped inches away from the white body standing in the middle of the road.

A slow sardonic smile as if to say he always knew Ridpath was going to stop.

He leant forward, resting his hands on the bonnet of the Vauxhall, his chest rising and falling with the pain of breathing. The man had blue eyes, the pale blue standing out in stark contrast to the white skin of the face and the dark, almost jet-black, hair.

But Ridpath's eyes were drawn to a bright blue pair of angel's wings tattooed across the chest, outstretched as if ready to take flight.

Ridpath heard a sharp screech behind him, the squeal of brakes. He glanced in the rear-view mirror. A white van was racing towards him. Strangely, at that moment he remembered the old stickers on car mirrors. 'Vehicles may look bigger than they are.'

But this one *was* big and it was coming straight at him.

The screech of brakes was getting louder. Ridpath braced himself for the impact, pushing his body deeper into the leather seat.

The man continued to stare at him with his blue eyes.

Then silence.

No violent smack of bonnet against boot.

No sickening crunch of metal on metal.

No whiplash as the neck muscles fought to keep the head upright.

Ridpath checked his rear-view mirror. The van had stopped behind him with a foot to spare, the orange warning lights flashing brightly.

Two loud, long beeps of a horn shouted anger at Ridpath's car, stationary in the middle lane of a motorway.

Ridpath stared at the man in front of him through the wind-screen. For some reason, the wipers decided at that moment to swoosh across the glass, removing a film of dust and dirt.

Instantly, the man's face became clearer. He glanced at Ridpath and then looked fearfully to his right, towards the hard shoulder.

Ridpath followed his eyes.

Another man was standing there, slightly older, stockier, dressed in a black hoodie and jeans and holding a gun in his right hand. A breath of wind blew for a second and the man's hood lifted away from his face.

Hard features, like an avenging angel.

A lorry on the inside lane wiped across Ridpath's vision, blocking the man with the gun from view.

The young man in front of his car took his hands off Ridpath's bonnet and began to run to his left, taking two paces before he was hit by a green articulated lorry.

The body sailed up into the air like a rag doll being thrown away by a bad-tempered child, landing with a sickening thud on the tarmac.

# Chapter Two

Ridpath sat there, stunned.

The lorry skidded to a halt, jack-knifing around the young man on the ground, the trailer narrowly missing his body.

Ridpath reacted first. He flicked on his warning lights and opened the door, running to where the young man lay.

Just a few seconds ago this young man had been a living, breathing person. Now he was a just a heap of tangled remains; one arm bent backwards above the head, the right leg at an impossible angle to the torso. Ridpath stared at the face, or what remained of it.

The head must have been caught by a wing mirror; a deep gash lay across the middle of the skull. Blood oozed from between the broken edges of the wound. Inside, bright white bone flecked with blood peeped through the tangled hair and skin.

Ridpath looked away from the body. Cars were still cruising slowly past in the inside lane, drivers gawking at the twisted remains lying on the dark grey road.

He searched the hard shoulder for the man with the gun.

Nothing.

Just a wooden fence protecting the motorists from the land-scaped woods of Sale Water Park.

He scanned up and down the motorway.

Still nothing.

Where had the man gone?

'I couldn't do nowt, he just ran in front of me truck.'

A man standing in front of him, wearing a checked shirt with sleeves rolled up to reveal tattooed arms. The lorry driver.

'I didn't see him.'

Ridpath bit his tongue. Behind him, the impatient noise of honking from drivers getting louder as it spread from one car to another.

He ignored them, kneeling down beside the body, checking the wrist for a pulse.

Nothing.

At the side, the cars still crawling past on the inside lane. Ridpath saw a child, his face pressed to the rear window, staring wide-eyed and open-mouthed at the mess of limbs lying at Ridpath's feet.

He had to do something.

'This is a crime scene. Do you have breakdown kit?'

The driver nodded.

'Use it to block the inside lane. Don't let anybody past. Understand?'

The driver nodded again, staring down at the body beneath his feet.

'Hurry, man.'

The lorry driver ran back to his cab.

Ridpath reached for his mobile phone, dialling 999.

'Emergency, which service?'

'Police and ambulance.'

'Putting you through.'

There was a buzz down the line for a second before a female voice came on the line. 'Police, what is the nature of your emergency?'

Ridpath kept his voice calm. 'This is Detective Inspector Thomas Ridpath one-nine-eight-seven, comms. Major incident on M60 eastbound opposite Sale Water Park at B 11.0. Request urgent assistance from police and ambulance, plus an armed tactical response team and a scene of crime unit. Over.'

A buzz of silence.

'M60 Motorway Control are aware of the incident, DI Ridpath. Traffic and medical responders are arriving asap. ETA two minutes. Over.'

The accident and the subsequent build-up in traffic must have been spotted on CCTV. Ridpath stared down the motorway. A tall yellow pylon with a camera on top was focused on the road.

'Repeat again, comms. Request armed tactical team asap as well as a SOC unit. Armed man with gun spotted on hard shoulder. Over'

'Message received, DI Ridpath. Tactical team informed and the SOC unit. Will confirm time of arrival asap. Over.'

Ridpath clicked off the phone and ran to the rear of his car, opening the boot to pull out his triangular warning sign. The lorry driver was vainly trying to stop a Mercedes from swerving around him using the hard shoulder to get past. The driver was shouting insults through his open window.

Ridpath ran in front of the Mercedes placing his warning sign in front of the car.

The old man leant out of his window. 'What do you think you're bloody doing?' Get that thing out of my way.'

He pulled out his warrant card, flashing it at the driver. 'Detective Inspector Ridpath, Greater Manchester Police Major Incident Team. You will wait here and not move your car. If you do, you will be charged with failing to stop at the scene of an accident. Do you understand... sir?'

The man meekly nodded.

'Switch off your engine and don't start it again until told to do so by a police officer. Do I make myself clear?'

Quickly the man reached forward and killed his engine, placing both hands on top of his steering wheel.

Ridpath ran to the lorry driver.

'They wouldn't bloody stop.'

'Don't worry, they have now.'

Ridpath peered over the top of a black Volkswagen. Behind it cars were beginning to pile up. A shimmer of blue exhaust rising like heat waves into the April sky.

'You stay here, make sure nobody drives past.'

'I couldn't do nothing. He just ran straight in front of me.'

He patted the man on the back. 'Just make sure nobody drives past.'

Ridpath ran towards the hard shoulder. Was this where the man with the gun was standing? He looked up and down the motorway. It could be anywhere within a hundred yards of here. He tried to remember the background behind the man, but all he saw were trees and a wooden fence.

His phone rang. 'DI Ridpath.'

'Comms here, Ridpath. Armed tactical squad ETA in twelve minutes. Traffic and ambulance in two minutes. Still waiting on SOC response. Over.'

Ridpath pulled the phone away from his ear. In the distance, the reassuring discordant wail of sirens.

'I can hear them, comms.'

'How many injured?'

'Just one man. I think he's dead.'

'Will inform first responders and Traffic. Over.'

'Thank you, comms. Over.'

The sirens were already getting louder. Ridpath glanced across at the lorry driver, still standing in the middle of the inside lane with his arms spread wide as if herding recalcitrant cattle, the cars in front of him belching blue smoke.

He ran back to the body lying crumpled on the tarmac of the M60. Blood seeped from the man's injuries, pooling on the road. From the head a soup of blood and brains drenched his right shoulder. The angel's wings were still there, untouched by the accident. For some reason, the tattoo was bluer now against the white skin and the grey background of the tarmac.

A motorbike pulled up on the hard shoulder. A paramedic took off his helmet and calmly gathered his case before walking across the road and kneeling next to the body.

'How long?' asked the paramedic in a broad Scottish accent.

'How long what?'

'How long since the accident?'

Ridpath kicked himself. In the chaos, he hadn't made a note of the time. 'I'm not sure. About seven minutes I think.'

The first responder noted it on his pad, before slipping on a pair of light green gloves. He reached over and placed his fingers on the young man's neck, leaving them there for fifteen seconds while he stared at his watch.

'He's dead. Looks like it was instantaneous. Was he hit by that?'

The paramedic pointed to the artic.

'Ran right in front of it.'

The paramedic wasn't listening to his answer but writing something on his response sheet.

'And your name is?'

'Thomas Ridpath. DI Thomas Ridpath.'

Out of the corner of his eye, Ridpath could see a police car pull up on the hard shoulder behind the parked Mercedes. A large burly man wearing uniform opened the car door, stepped out and slowly walked to move the sign to one side.

'Oi, you, leave that there,' Ridpath shouted. He ran towards the policeman waving his arms. 'Don't move forward, this is a crime scene.'

'Who do you think you're shouting at?'

'You can't drive on the hard shoulder, it's a crime scene.'

'And who do you think you bloody are to give me orders?'

Ridpath pulled out his warrant card.

The policeman stared at the card and sniffed. 'Well, I'm Chief Inspector Harold Todd, in charge of traffic for Greater Manchester. And we're going to open this road, Sunny Jim.'

# Chapter Three

Ridpath moved in front of the superior officer. 'With all due respect, sir. You can't do that.'

'With all due respect, son, I can.' He turned and waved to his officers arriving in their orange-striped BMWs.

'Sir, there is an armed man in this area. I have called for support from an armed response team and an SOC unit.'

The chief inspector turned slowly towards him, pointing back over his shoulder to the line of cars jamming the road.

'See that son. It's Wednesday, there's a game on at Old Trafford and it's the busiest traffic time of the week on the M60. The cars already tailback three miles to the Trafford Centre. Soon the jam will extend over Barton Bridge and start to block the exit roads from the M62, M61, M6 and every other bloody road in north Manchester.' He smiled. 'Do you really want to be responsible, lad?'

Ridpath closed his eyes. Why did these things always happen to him? Should he just forget it, let this man take charge, keep the traffic flowing?

'Well, son?' Chief Inspector Harold Todd had a smug smile on his face.

'I'm not your son. I am a serving officer with the Greater Manchester Police. This is a crime scene and the road will remain closed until I am told it is no longer needed by the senior investigating officer.'

Harold Todd smiled again. 'Listen…?'

'Ridpath, Detective Inspector Thomas Ridpath.'

'Listen…,' the voice was emollient now, 'nobody is going to thank you for this. Is your career worth risking for some druggie who's so off his tree he's decided to play chicken on the M60?'

Ridpath flashed back to the moment when the young man was leaning with his hands on the bonnet of his car, the blue eyes pained with fear. Was his career worth it?

'Well, is it?'

Ridpath took a deep breath before answering. 'This is a crime scene… sir.'

'On your own head be it.' He turned back to the traffic officers standing beside the open doors of their cars, shouting. 'Implement Operation Trident. Block all entrances onto the M60 from Junctions 7 through to 15. Route southbound traffic from the M61 towards the eastern side of the ring road. Move it.'

The traffic officers stared at each other, then leapt back in their cars, reversing to the next slip road.

Chief Inspector Harold Todd walked slowly back to his car shaking his head, leaving Ridpath all alone on the hard shoulder. In the nearby cars families were staring at him, children watching through the glass of the rear windows. The man in the white van who had nearly rear-ended him tapping his fingers impatiently on the steering wheel.

As the sun began to set and the sidelights shined through the fog of car exhaust, a bleating of car horns echoed down the M60 like lost lambs in search of their mother.

Ridpath ran back towards the body lying in the middle of the M60.

'Oi, how long do I have to stand here like a bloody scare-crow?'

It was the lorry driver, forehead dripping with sweat, arms still outstretched, a lion tamer holding a pack of beasts at bay.

Ridpath shrugged his shoulders, putting his mobile phone to his mouth. He called the last number and was put through to the comms officer. 'How long till the armed response team arrive, comms?'

'ETA uncertain, heavy traffic.'

'I know there's heavy traffic, I'm the one who's causing it,' he shouted down the phone. Ridpath cursed himself for losing his temper.

'Two minutes. You should be able to hear them now. MIT is on its way too. Over.'

'Who's in charge? Over.'

'Just a minute. It's a Detective Chief Inspector Charles Whitworth. Over.'

Ridpath smiled to himself. Of all people on duty tonight, it had to be Charlie Whitworth. Above the cacophony of idling engines Ridpath could hear more sirens approaching at speed down the hard shoulder. 'Thank you, comms,' he said before switching off his mobile phone.

The first responder was still standing over the crumpled body of the young man. 'Ambulance will be here in two minutes.'

'Too late for him.'

'Look I got here as quickly as I could. See, eight minutes response time.' He pointed to the time on his log sheet.

'Still too late,' said Ridpath turning away.

The armed response team and an unmarked Ford were squeezing past the cars of the traffic police on the hard shoulder, pulling up short of the red triangle beyond the parked Mercedes. Armed men began to pile out of the rear doors, fanning out along the motorway.

Ridpath ran to meet them, holding up his warrant card. 'Police, DI Ridpath.'

'You called it in? Where's the perp?' The officer in charge was dressed in black combat fatigues and carrying a Heckler and Koch sub-machine gun across his chest. The bottom part of his face was covered but the words came out clear and forceful.

'He was standing somewhere along the hard shoulder…'

'Somewhere?' the officer interrupted.

'I was driving past. I didn't see exactly where.'

'Shots fired?'

Ridpath shook his head. 'No, I didn't see or hear any.'

The officer pointed to the body. 'He's been wounded?'

Again, Ridpath shook his head. 'Run down by a lorry. Look, I think he was being chased by an armed man and that's why he ran across the road.'

'You think?'

Ridpath frowned. 'He was being chased by an armed man.'

'What weapon?'

'A handgun.'

'Revolver or automatic?'

Ridpath closed his eyes. The image of the man standing on the hard shoulder holding the gun in his right hand flashed into his mind.'

'Automatic... I think.'

'Which way did he run?'

'I don't know. By the time, I looked again, he had vanished.'

The officer nodded once and then turned to his men. 'Fan out. We're going to search the Water Park. You two, start from Junction 7. Briggs and Miles you start at Rifle Road, walk through Sale Ees and meet up with Jackson and Wright. The rest of you with me. Hurry, lads, I want this place secure before it goes dark.'

An unmarked Vauxhall was parking 150 yards away on the hard shoulder. Ridpath could see Charlie Whitworth jogging towards him slowly, followed by the usual suspects of DI Make-peace, DS Hardy, DS Butcher and a new man he'd never seen before.

Whitworth was out of breath when he arrived. 'Ridpath. I might have bloody guessed you'd be behind this shower of shit.'

# Chapter Four

'Hello, Charlie, you don't know how glad I am to see you.'

Ridpath had once been one of Charlie's blue-eyed boys but had collapsed during a major investigation when the cancer had taken hold. Nine months afterwards, in remission and cleared by occupational health, he had gone back to work to find he had been temporarily assigned to the Coroner's Office rather than return to his old job. Unfortunately, during the recent Beast of Manchester case, Ridpath had been forced to re-investigate one of his boss's old cases. Nobody liked to be proved wrong, especially not Charlie Whitworth.

'Wish I could say the same to you. I've just had the Assistant Chief Constable on the blower to me. Apparently, you've managed to piss off the head of Traffic. Now, I know old Harold, he's an officious old tosser but he's a good copper. Old school, you know what I mean?'

They began walking toward the body lying in the road.

'Take me through what happened.'

Ridpath told the story with all the detail he could remember.

'You're certain the man was armed?'

'Certain.'

'And the kid just ran across the road, straight in front of this bloody artic?'

'No, he stopped in front of my car first. Resting his hands on my bonnet and then he ran off to be hit by the lorry.'

'Was he off his face?'

Ridpath thought back to the wild blue eyes. 'Could have been, I'm not sure.'

'Acid, E, Coke, PCP, Ket?'

'Don't know, boss.'

They were standing over the body.

'Any ID?'

The first responder looked down at the naked body just clad in its blue boxers and shook his head. 'Where'd he keep it?'

The pool of blood around the head was larger now, the gash in the skull already covered in congealed lumps of blood and brain.

'Poor sod. Not a nice way to go. Where's the bloody pathologist?'

'He's on his way, boss,' answered Dave Hardy, 'stuck in traffic.'

'And the SOC team?'

'Same, boss.'

Charlie Whitworth ran his hand through his thinning hair. 'Jesus. And it would have to be a bloody football night too.'

Another detective, somebody Ridpath hadn't seen before, ran up. 'The natives are getting restless boss.'

People had started getting out of their cars, congregating in groups and looking towards the jack-knifed lorry and the body lying in the middle of the road. Behind them, the sound of beeping horns was growing louder and louder.

'Right, Alan, you interview the lorry driver. Get a full description of what he saw. Harry and Dave you two go round the front three ranks of cars. I want full witness statements. Make sure you get names and addresses as well as licence details. And check if any of them have dash cam. Ronnie, I want you to get the CCTV from the motorway control room. I need to look at the footage asap.'

'Yes, boss.'

The detectives hurried off leaving Ridpath and Charlie Whitworth still standing over the dead body.

'Are you sure this wasn't a druggie who's just decided to take a stroll across the busiest road in Manchester?'

'Certain, boss. I saw a man with a gun.'

Charlie's bottom lip came up and covered his moustache. 'Right,' he said finally. 'You can go back to the station with John Snow. I want a full signed witness statement from you tonight. Plus you can work with E-Fit to create a picture of the perp.'

'What about…?'

Before Ridpath could finish a convoy of police cars, led by a sleek black BMW, was heading straight towards them on the empty road in front, driving the wrong way down the M60.

'Oh shit, just what I needed…' said Charlie, shaking his head.

# Chapter Five

The door of the black BMW opened and a long pair of elegant legs in black heels placed themselves carefully on the tarmac of the motorway. The legs were followed by a woman of medium height, her hair cut in a severe blonde bob as if she had just stepped out of a hair salon a few minutes ago.

From another car the burly shape of Harold Todd joined the woman and together they both strode down the motorway past the jack-knifed lorry, Todd keeping one yard behind in imitation of Prince Philip.

'Evening, ma'am.'

'Evening Charlie. Is this your pile of shit?'

'I... I...'

For the first time, Ridpath saw Charlie Whitworth was lost for words.

The blonde bob turned round to face him.

'Hello, Ridpath, long time no see. How come you're involved?'

Charlie's eyes narrowed. 'You two know each other?'

The woman answered for him. 'We met at the training school. I was young Ridpath's lecturer in criminal law. When was it? 2006?'

'2007, ma'am.'

What Ridpath didn't mention was they had slept together on the last night of the course. A drunken fumbling after a night in the pub. He winced as he still remembered the mess her nails had made to his back. This was before he met and fell in love with Polly of course. Somehow it seemed such a long time ago.

Claire Trent had hardly changed in the last eleven years. Either she practised a strict diet and exercise regime, or she used an awful lot of Botox.

Ridpath checked her forehead. Not a wrinkle or frown to be seen.

'You look surprised, Ridpath. Didn't Charlie tell you? I took over from John Gorman as Head of MIT yesterday.'

So she was his new guvnor. Even though he was temporarily attached to the Coroner's Office, officially he was still part of MIT, retaining his inspector rank.

Perhaps the world was finally turning in his favour. And then his tower of optimism came tumbling down as quickly as it had been erected.

'So who's responsible for this shower of shit?'

Everybody, including the first responder, stared at him.

'You reported seeing an armed man on the hard shoulder, Ridpath?'

'Yes, ma'am.'

'An armed response team are searching Sale Water Park, ma'am,' interjected Charlie, quickly taking implicit credit.

She ignored her second in command, continuing to stare at Ridpath. 'Are you sure?'

He nodded. 'I was driving in the middle lane but I'm pretty sure.'

'Pretty sure or sure?'

Ridpath replayed the image in his mind of the man's face and the gun in his hand. 'Sure,' he finally said.

'Right, Harold. This is a crime scene. Get the pathologist and the SOC team to check out the body. And set up a tent around it. Too many bloody gawkers here.'

'But, the traffic…'

'Sorry, Harold, can't be helped. We'll be as quick as we can.'

Over the chief superintendent's shoulder Ridpath could see three Tyvex clothed men walking towards the dead body carrying their kit. In front, a shorter man looking like a teenager led the way.

'Where do I sign in?' asked the teenager.

'And who are you?'

'I'm Dr Schofield, the pathologist.' He pointed back over his shoulder. 'Sophie Cook will be the crime scene manager.'

'Organise a cordon around the body and set up the usual protocols Charlie,' said Claire Trent.

'Yes, ma'am.'

'And you, Ridpath. Back to the station. I want a detailed witness statement on my desk this evening. And give a description to E-Fit,' she said, unknowingly echoing Charlie Whitworth's previous order.

Despite their previous relationship the voice was cold and businesslike. 'Yes, ma'am,' was all he answered. 'And one other thing, ma'am. The victim touched the bonnet of my car with his hands. You might want to take the prints.'

'You heard that, Sophie?' Claire Trent shouted at the crime scene manager.

'Noted, ma'am,' was the instant response.

'And you lot stop calling me ma'am. I'm not the bloody queen, not yet anyway. Boss or Guvnor will do.'

'Yes, ma'am,' answered Charlie Whitworth.

Claire Trent eyed him suspiciously. 'Well, what are you waiting for? Get a bloody move on.'

## Chapter Six

He was sitting forward in the kitchen chair, elbows resting on his knees, furiously smoking a cigarette.

'You bloody fool, how did he escape?' She lunged forward snatching the cigarette from between his fingers and running the lit end under the tap. 'I told you before I can't stand you smoking too much. It stinks the whole house out.' She turned back to face him. 'Well?'

'I went for a walk, when I got back I found he'd managed to escape from the ropes.'

'You went out for a walk?' She ran her fingers through her long blonde hair, 'I told you never to leave him alone. Never to leave any of them alone.'

'But you don't understand. It gets so boring here. I needed fresh air.'

She knelt in front of him, resting her hands on his. 'Your one job was to guard him. Keep him doped up so he didn't even think about escaping.'

'He must have worked out his water was spiked. Gerard always was smart.'

She stood up again. 'Tell me what happened.'

'I came back and checked the cellar as I always do. Usually he's asleep...'

'Ambien has that effect on people.'

He stared at her for a second before continuing. 'But this time, he wasn't there. The rope was lying in two pieces on the floor.'

'How did he cut it?'

The man threw his hands in the air. 'I don't bloody know.'

'Why was the door open?'

The man looked down at the floor. 'I forgot to lock it,' he whispered.

'I told you to watch him. Jesus…'

'I checked the rest of the cellar in case he was hiding…'

'But he wasn't…'

'So I grabbed the gun and went after him.'

'Let's get this right. You walked out in full daylight carrying a loaded gun?'

He nodded.

'Talk about stupidity. What if somebody saw you?'

'What else was I supposed to do? Let him run away and talk to the police? They'd be here in five minutes.'

She stayed silent.

'Anyway, I guessed he hadn't been gone long, the blanket was still warm, I ran after him.'

'How'd you know which way he went?'

'I didn't.' He shrugged his shoulders. 'I was lucky I guess.'

'And?'

'And after about five minutes I spotted him running up the path to the motorway. He was moving pretty slowly, I guess there was still some of the drug in his system.'

'So you went after him?'

'I ran to the motorway. He must have known about the gap in the fence…'

'Most people do.'

'As I went through it he was just stepping over the crash barrier onto the hard shoulder. I think he had this idea he was going to flag down one of the cars, but they were all going too fast. He ran out into the road, one car narrowly missed him, but he managed to stop another. I ran towards him.'

'Did anybody see you?'

'I don't think so. The traffic was heavy. Anyway, he must have seen me because then he ran towards the far lane and was hit by a truck.'

'Is he dead?'

'I didn't hang around to check but when you're hit by a forty-ton artic going at speed, you don't survive.'

'Nobody saw you?'

He nodded. 'I wasn't there long.'

She ran her fingers through her hair again. 'What about the motorway cameras?'

'I'm sure they saw the accident, but I stayed close to the fence and didn't go onto the hard shoulder.'

'I suppose that's one saving grace from this clusterfuck.'

'At least it saves us killing him. I quite liked Gerard, he made me laugh.'

She knelt down next to him again. 'Listen, you don't get close to the people we take, understand?'

He nodded.

'I wanted us to kill him. Make him suffer. Even more, I wanted them to know he'd been killed. Now it just looks like an accident.'

'But he's dead anyway, I think...'

She put a long, elegant finger across his lips. 'Listen, Reggie, you're my brother but I do the thinking. We've got a plan and we're going to put into action. You're here to make it happen. Do you understand?'

He nodded again.

'Just do whatever I tell you. We've got a lot of work to do in the next few days. We're going to make them pay for what they did.'

# Chapter Seven

Ridpath was at the station giving his statement when it struck him like a sledgehammer. 'Oh shit.' He checked the large clock on wall. 10:35 p.m. 'Is that the right time?'

The new detective, John Snow, who was taking the details, glanced over his shoulder. 'Nah, it's always slow. The real time is...' he flicked up his sleeve revealing a gigantic black chronometer, '...10:47 and twenty-three seconds.'

'Shit,' mumbled Ridpath under his breath. 'Look, do you mind if we take a break. I've got to make a call.'

'No problem. More coffee?'

Ridpath shook his head. 'I'll be awake until next Tuesday if I drink any more.'

DC Snow shuffled off in search of fresh coffee for himself. Ridpath took out his phone. No calls. Was that good or bad?

He rang Polly's number and was immediately transferred to a machine. 'Hello, you've reached Polly Lam, you know the drill.' Then a pause. 'But if that's Ridpath, you should be ashamed of yourself. Your daughter is inconsolable. Bastard.'

It was bad.

He rang again, getting the same message. After the beep he left one of his own. 'Look, I'm really sorry Polly. I was involved in an accident driving back from Teesside. Please ask Eve to forgive me. And, in case you ask, I'm OK.'

He switched off his phone. The call came five seconds later.

'Are you OK? Are you hurt?'

'No, I'm fine.'

'Really?'

'Really, I'm fine. I witnessed somebody being killed on the motorway so I'm now at the station giving a statement.'

There was a pause on the other end of the phone. 'So you weren't actually involved in the accident?'

'No, I...'

'You didn't crash your car or hit anybody?'

'No, like I said, I...'

'And you weren't injured at all? Not even a sprained, lying tongue?'

'Don't be like that Polly...'

'Your daughter has been waiting for you since 6:30 this evening.'

'I know, I'm sorry... I...'

'No phone call. Nothing.'

'I had to give a statement and it slipped my mind.'

Another pause. 'Seems like we're always slipping through the cracks in your mind, Ridpath. Maybe, you should think about us just once in a while.'

'I'll call her tomorrow to explain.'

'I don't know if she wants to talk to you.'

'Please, Polly, she's ten years old, she has to talk to me.'

There was long sigh down the end of the phone. 'You just don't get it, do you, Ridpath?'

Then there was the buzzing sound indicating she had ended the call. Ridpath thought about phoning back, but just as he was about to press the button Charlie Whitworth entered the interview room.

He sat down in front of Ridpath. Without saying a word, he picked up the witness statement and began to read it. After he had finished, he put it down gently on the table. His bottom lip came up to meet the bottom of his moustache. 'Is that it, Ridpath?'

'Yes, Charlie. Except the E-Fit of the man with the gun hasn't been attached.'

The eyes flicked up from the statement and stared straight at Ridpath. 'We've got a problem.'

'Just one, Charlie?'

'Nah, about twenty actually.'

Charlie's meaty hand came up with the thumb pointing upwards. 'Number one. The mayor has been on the blower to the chief constable.'

'What does he want?'

'Your guts. We finally cleared the scene at 9:30 p.m. By that time the traffic jam stretched seventeen miles, all the way to Bolton. The game started half full, most of the bloody fans stuck on the M60. The mayor's not a happy camper, and if he's not happy, the chief gets it in the ear. You should know that shit flows downhill, Ridpath, and at the moment there's a bloody avalanche of it heading your way.'

'I know what I saw, boss.'

'Number two.' The index finger flicked up. 'CCTV doesn't show anybody standing on the hard shoulder. We see the victim come from the left, a car swerving around him, you braking to a stop. Thank God, you were under the speed limit. The victim leaning on your car for a couple of seconds and then the lorry hitting him.'

'There's nobody on the hard shoulder?'

Charlie shook his head. 'Nobody.'

Ridpath thought quickly. 'Does the CCTV show the other side of the barrier?'

'You mean the crash barrier before the hard shoulder? Nah, it just focuses on the road.'

'The man may have been on the other side of the barrier...'

'So now you're changing your story?'

'No, I'm not. It happened so quickly...I was driving in the middle lane and this young man suddenly ran straight out in front of me.'

'So when did you see the man with the gun?'

'When I stopped. The young man had his hands on my bonnet and he glanced across to his right. I followed where he was looking.'

Charlie sighed. 'Number three. The lorry driver said he saw nobody, only the man he hit with his lorry. He's still a bit of a mess though. He remembers nothing except the sound of his wing mirror carving into the young man's skull.'

'He was in the outside lane. He wouldn't have seen anything.'

'The poor sod is going to lose his licence though. We breathalysed him. He was over.'

'There was nothing he could have done even if he'd been stone cold sober.'

'Doesn't matter, he's toast. Number four. No other driver in any of the cars behind you reports seeing a man on the hard shoulder or behind the barrier.'

'What about the car on the inside lane. The one that swerved out of the way?'

'We haven't been able to locate him yet.'

'Why? You must have the number plate from the CCTV?'

'It was fake. No records for that plate.'

'No wonder he didn't stop after the accident. He must have seen everything.' Ridpath thought for a moment. 'What about ANPR? You must be able to track him?'

'Don't teach me how to do my job, Ridpath.'

'I'm not, Charlie, it's just—'

'We're looking through the footage as we speak. But if he left the motorway and went on side roads…'

'There'll be fewer cameras.'

'At least I trained you well.' The finger went up again. 'Number five. The armed response team found nothing in Sale Water Park except three courting couples and a gross of used johnnies. They felt, and I quote, "it was a waste of police time and scarce resources". End quote.'

'I know what I saw, Charlie. There was a man with a handgun chasing our vic. Have we ID'd him yet?'

'The vic?' Charlie shook his head. 'We'll release a picture tomorrow to the *Evening News* and hope somebody comes forward. But my bet is he was a druggie who thought he was in the middle of paradise rather than in the middle of the M60.'

'I don't think so, Charlie. He was scared for his life. That's why he was running. What would be so frightening you would run across one of the busiest roads in the north of England in the middle of rush hour?'

'Why are you asking me? I'm not a bloody clairvoyant.'

# Chapter Eight

After Ridpath had left Charlie Whitworth sat alone in his office re-reading Ridpath's statement. There were too many unanswered questions.

Why had nobody else seen the man beside the M60?

Why was the victim running across the road in the first place?

Why there?

And why then?

He pulled out a bottle of whisky from the drawer, pouring a large splash into an empty mug on his desk. Ridpath wasn't an officer given to exaggeration. In fact before his illness he had been one of MIT's rising stars; smart, energetic and above all, persistent.

It was all bollocks this Sherlock Holmes stuff. Police work was all about perseverance; chasing down leads, following up on details, keeping going when all others have given up.

It wasn't about hunches or guesses or leaps of imagination but dogged, determined bloody-mindedness that solved a case and put away criminals. It was all about chasing evidence until it was so damning even the most stupid of juries, and there were a lot of those, had no option but to convict.

He took a large slug of whisky from the mug, enjoying the hit on the back of his throat. His bottom lip came up to taste the drops of liquid gold stuck to his moustache.

He could go home now, the wife would be asleep, snoring as she always did.

He sat still for a moment, listening to the noises of a police station at night. In the distance, a siren rushing to some real or imagined emergency. Closer, the tapping of a keyboard as one of the night shift completed his paperwork. In his office, the slight whirr of his ancient desktop as the fan fought to keep it cool.

He missed the kids. One was on a gap year in Australia, working on some fruit farm somewhere. Last week, on the phone call, she said she had met some Aussie and might not come back. Little Sam, his favourite. Always easygoing, always loving even as a child. She had found love easier than he ever had. Shame it had to be on the other side of the world.

The other, Jane, still at university studying sociology. What was the point in that? Can't get a bloody job with a degree in sociology. But she had insisted and now she hardly spoke to him. And when they did, they argued. Apparently he was an active 'participant in the hegemonic forces of a reactionary state'. Whatever that meant.

He took another longer slurp of the whisky. She was too like him was Jane. Possibly more dogged, more determined than even he was.

He poured another measure of whisky into the mug. No point in going home yet. The wife would be asleep whatever time it was.

He often wondered if she used sleep as a weapon against him. A way of avoiding any interaction. After twenty-five years of marriage it wasn't surprising. He didn't think he could stand being with him that long either.

Twenty-five years. Almost as long as he had been a copper.

Not many left now. John Gorman was gone. The best copper he had ever known and the best man. After the Beast of Manchester case he had taken early retirement.

What a bloody waste.

He raised the mug up high. 'Here's to you, John, and the allotment.'

There was no taste in the whisky any more. No bite at the back of the throat. He laughed to himself. A bit like him really.

What to do about Ridpath? If Claire Trent had her way he would be hung out to dry. Somebody had to be the fall guy for this evening's fiasco and what better person than the man who caused it?

He would try to protect him of course, but in the new GMP blame was everything. It wasn't about how good a copper you were, but about how many arses you licked and how many balls you rubbed.

He took another long draught of whisky.

'Here's to survival,' he said to the four walls.

He would go home soon, but not just yet.

## Chapter Nine

Ridpath sat in his empty house, staring at a blank TV screen. He had tried to ring Polly three times but she hadn't answered. Instead the infernal answering machine had simply reminded him of her voice and the last damning word.

Bastard.

A wave of tiredness washed over him. He should have rung them to explain. *He should have rung them.*

Slowly he levered himself out of the chair and hobbled over to the cabinet to fix himself a Laphroaig. His whole body felt like he had just gone ten rounds with Mike Tyson. Even his ear had been bitten off by Claire Trent when she saw him back at the station.

'For your sake, there'd better be a man with a gun, Ridpath. Otherwise, you can kiss your career goodbye. Even the coroner will have nothing to do with you after I'm finished.'

He raised the glass to his lips. 'Cheers, Claire. Up yours.'

He drank a large mouthful down in one gulp, enjoying the bite of honey at the back of his throat, followed by a tingle down his spine as if somebody had just danced on his grave.

'Perhaps it was Claire Trent in her spiked heels,' he said out loud.

The empty house didn't answer him.

Once again his mind turned to that moment, seeing himself sitting in the car, facing the young man with the angel wings tattooed on his chest. It was like he was watching himself from outside the car. Seeing the young man's head turn, his own following the man's line of sight. Staring at the hoodie with the gun in his right hand. It was a gun, not a knife, nor a hammer, nor anything else.

A gun. An automatic. A matt black killer.

The young man's eyes widening with fear and then taking two steps away, straight into the oncoming artic. The wing mirror cleaving the skull in two, the body flying through the air, landing in a misshapen lump ten yards in front of his car.

Not moving. Still.

He swallowed another large mouthful of Laphroaig.

He had seen it, hadn't he? A man with a gun in his right hand. A hard face revealed as the hoodie blew off in the wind.

It wasn't his imagination.

It wasn't the drugs.

The man had been standing there, staring at the victim.

Why hadn't anybody else seen him?

# Day Two

*Thursday, April 19, 2018*

# Chapter Ten

The following morning Ridpath reached over to hug his wife closer to him as the morning light crept between the slender gap in the curtains. His arm wrapped around her shoulders and her hair touched his cheek. He smelt the aroma of her shampoo; sweet, clean with a hint of apple blossom. He edged forward wanting to feel the warmth and softness of her body against his.

But she wasn't there.

He sat up in bed, immediately feeling a huge sense of loneliness wash over him. He opened his eyes, disoriented for a moment, unable to make sense of his surroundings. The white wardrobe and matching dresser bought from Ikea looked alien, as if he had never seen them before. His wife's things were still arrayed neatly on top of the dresser; various creams and masks, lipstick, facial cleanser, a brush with a few dark hairs struggling to escape its bristles.

He shook his head.

He was at home. Their home.

*Pull yourself together, Ridpath.*

He stumbled downstairs still tasting the dregs of the Laphroaig pasted to the inside of his mouth and teeth. He had sat up till 2:30 a.m. staring into mid-air, going over the events of the day again and again, all chased down with more glasses of whisky.

Far too many glasses of whisky.

He put the kettle on and absent-mindedly switched on the TV. The mayor of Manchester was talking; hair swept back, tie crisply tied in a half Oxford, elegantly tailored jacket fastened tightly against an even tighter waist.

Ridpath turned up the sound.

'…The events of yesterday indicate the police response to the accident during rush hour was woefully negligent. I will be seeking a full explanation from the chief constable this morning and, if none is forthcoming, appointing an independent commission into the affair.'

An off-screen presenter asked a question. 'But surely the massive traffic jams caused by the accident point to a problem with traffic management and traffic planning?'

'Not at all, Wendy. Normally traffic flows smoothly even at the busiest times along the M60. Our recent improvements have increased traffic flow by 28 per cent. I will be looking at the way the police responded to the accident. There is no way people should be stuck in a traffic jam for four hours when all they want to do is get home to their wife and kids or go and see a football match.'

'Thank you, mayor.'

Ridpath switched the TV off, he couldn't listen to it any more. So that's how they were spinning it now. A traffic accident. No mention of a crime scene or a man with a gun.

Was he being hung out to dry?

Time to go to the coroner's office. He showered and dressed quickly, grabbing his keys from the hall table.

They weren't there.

And then he remembered the car was still being checked for fingerprints by the SOC team.

Shit.

He called a minicab and instructed the driver to take the M60 to Stockfield. Within minutes they were driving past the location of yesterday's events.

Ridpath sat up in the back of the cab, peering out of the rear window. He had difficulty finding exactly where the accident had happened. Nothing marked the spot. No tents remained on the motorway. No coppers scoured the area around the hard shoulder for evidence. No police at all.

The traffic moved smoothly, drivers totally oblivious to the events of the night before.

It was like nothing had ever happened.

The driver stared at him in the rear-view mirror. 'Accident here last night,' he said as they raced past the scene.

'I know.'

'I got caught in the tailback with a fare from the Trafford Centre. Three bloomin' hours we were stuck in the jam. My fare had to get out and take a piss at the side of the road.'

The eyes staring at him in the rear-view mirror. Angry eyes.

'Whoever caused it should be shot. Bloody useless police. We pay them so much money and they can't even manage a traffic accident.'

Ridpath didn't answer. There was no point.

## Chapter Eleven

'Morning, Ridpath, you're early.'

'So are you. Is Mrs Challinor in her office?'

'Preparing for court. First day of the inquest on Ronald Wilson.'

Jenny, the office manager, was already in place behind the reception desk of the Coroner's Court. This morning her hair was pink and she wore a bright purple jumper which contrasted nicely with the green eyeshadow.

'Go careful when you see her. Mrs Challinor's on the warpath. She was stuck in traffic for an hour last night on her way home.'

Not another one, thought Ridpath. Time to tell her what happened.

He knocked on the door, heard the single word, 'Enter' and stepped right in. The head coroner was seated behind a neat desk going through a file, her nest of grey hair surrounding black-rimmed glasses.

A folded copy of the *Guardian* lay on the desk, showing the large headline. 'Manchester Gridlock.'

'Good morning, Ridpath. Good to see you, how was the course?'

Ridpath detected the slight scent of a different perfume, not her usual. Was it Shalimar?

'Pretty good, I learnt so much regarding the duties of a coroner's officer. Feel I understand what I'm supposed to be doing now.'

'Good. The trainer said you came top of the cohort. She seemed quite taken with you.'

Ridpath blushed. 'She was a good trainer – exact and challenging – I enjoyed it.' He paused for a moment. 'Actually, I'm here today because of something I learnt on the course.'

Margaret Challinor put her pen down. 'Go on…'

'I have to open a new case for us. The accident on the M60 last night.'

She leant forward and tapped the paper, 'I read about it. Even worse, I suffered it last night. You know they blocked entry onto the M60 for an hour.'

'May I?'

She nodded,

He pulled out a chair and told her the complete story. When he was finished, she was silent for a moment, then brushing her grey hair away from her eyes said. 'Are you sure there was a man with a gun?'

'Positive.'

'And we have no ID on the victim?'

'None.'

'The news is already calling it an "accident".' Margaret Challinor brushed her grey hair off her forehead impatiently. 'The designation of the cause of death is our job, not a reporter's nor is it the job of the mayor of Manchester. You'd better get Jenny to open a case on an unknown victim.'

'Will do. The post-mortem is at noon? Can I go?'

'It's unusual for a coroner's officer to attend but not disallowed. How's the workload?'

'I dunno yet. I'm sure there's a ton of emails. I'll sit down with Jenny this morning and get briefed on all the cases going through the system.' He paused scratching his nose. 'I'd like to go.'

'Don't make this personal, Ridpath, understand? Our job is to be dispassionate. To evaluate the evidence and come to a conclusion regarding the probable cause of death. Personal feelings should never come into it.'

'But it is personal, Mrs Challinor. I watched a man being killed by a forty-ton lorry because he was scared for his life, running away from a man with a gun.'

'Don't get too involved, Ridpath. Take it from me, it never helps.' She glanced at her watch. 'Time to start the inquest. I'd like you to join this one before you go to your post-mortem.'

'I should catch up with the workload.'

'I'll rephrase that, you're sitting in on this case. The investigation by the police has more holes than a Chinese bucket.'

# Chapter Twelve

Thirty minutes later he walked up the stairs to the court on the second floor.

After leaving the coroner he had been waylaid by the office manager and forced to read documents requiring his signature before she would let him escape.

The inquiry had already started as he slipped as quietly as he could through the doors.

The old building had recently been refurbished inside to bring it finally kicking and screaming into the twenty-first century, with flat screen TVs, microphones for the witnesses, a new jury box, Internet access and power points for the solicitors, and the latest projection equipment to display documents and evidence. All part of Mrs Challinor's desire to make it 'more responsive to modern needs'. However, the building still looked like some harsh Victorian school run by Mr Gradgrind whilst the coroner's procedures dated even further back to medieval times.

It was one of these procedures Ridpath heard as he sat down at the back of the court: the swearing of the oath.

Mrs Challinor turned her head slightly to notice his arrival, but didn't smile or offer any hint of a welcome. Instead, her concentration was focused on the man swearing the oath. A man Ridpath recognised as Detective Sergeant Tommy Harper.

He was dressed more neatly than Ridpath remembered, in a fresh shirt, suit and tie. He held a bible in his left hand and his right hand was held up palm forward as he gave the oath.

'I hearby swear to tell the truth, the whole truth, so help me God.'

In front of the coroner were three solicitors, each with a laptop open in front of them. Only two people sat in the visitors' area behind a length of purple rope. Ridpath didn't recognise them. No family seemed to be present.

Mrs Challinor spoke first. 'Please state your name and occupation for the court.'

The detective leant forward and spoke directly into the microphone. The sound came out loud and breathy. 'Detective Sergeant Thomas Harper, Greater Manchester Police, presently attached to J Division.'

'Thank you, Detective Sergeant. You are aware this inquest is an inquiry to into the death of Ronald Wilson; to establish when he died, why he died and how he came by his death. "How" can include the cause of death and the immediate events and circumstances leading to the death.'

'I am, ma'am.'

'I believe you are the investigating office in charge of the inquiry?'

Tommy Harper sat forward again, speaking directly into the mike. 'I am, ma'am.'

'Just stay where you are, Detective Sergeant, the mike will pick up your words without you moving closer.'

The policeman settled himself in his chair. 'Yes, ma'am, sorry ma'am.'

'How did you discover Ronald Wilson's body?'

'I didn't, ma'am.'

Mrs Challinor sighed. 'I'll rephrase the question. 'How was the body of the deceased discovered?'

'We received a phone call from dispatch at…' he checked his notes, '1:05 p.m. that some children had found a body floating in Lake Wingate…'

'What time did you arrive at the scene?'

'Me personally or the police?'

Mrs Challinor sighed. 'Let's do both, shall we?'

'A police sergeant from Reddish arrived at...' Harper checked his notes once more, '...1:26 p.m. No, I tell a lie, 1:21 p.m. Can't read my own handwriting.'

'And you?'

'I arrived at 1:43 p.m.'

'It took you a while?'

'I was investigating something else.'

Probably the bottom of a pint glass knowing Tommy, thought Ridpath.

'Tell me what happened next?'

'Well, I approached the lake...'

Mrs Challinor's eyebrow arched, 'There was no police cordon set up?'

'Not when I arrived. We set that up just before the pathologist arrived at 2:05 p.m.'

'So, children were walking around and looking at the body?'

'No, we kept them away as much as we could...'

While the detective sergeant was speaking, a tall blonde-haired woman dressed in black stepped forward and handed Mrs Challinor a note. This was Carol Oates, the area coroner.

Mrs Challinor opened it and said loudly enough for the court to hear. 'Are you sure?'

'Yes, coroner.'

'This is too bad, most unprofessional.' She placed the note down and spoke directly to the court. 'My apologies to the solicitors and to you, Detective Sergeant Harper, but I have just been told the pathologist, Dr Schofield, is unable to attend court today. An urgent case requires his immediate attention. He has also not yet finished his report into the death of Ronald Wilson.' She opened her desk diary and flicked through several pages. 'Accordingly, I hereby postpone this inquiry until...Thursday, April 26 at 10:00 a.m. in this court. My apologies once again. I will ensure the pathologist understands the necessity for his attendance at that time.'

With that polite but veiled threat she stood up and exited the court. Ridpath left quickly too, avoiding everybody as he rushed down the stairs to Mrs Challinor's office, hoping to see her before she was nabbed by somebody else.

He knocked on the door, waited for the word 'Enter' and stepped in.

Mrs Challinor had thrown her robe onto the back of her chair. She was pacing up and down, obviously livid. 'How dare the pathologist not bother to turn up? He promised me a report yesterday and it still hasn't arrived.' She turned to see Ridpath. 'What do you want?'

'I think his non-arrival has to do with me.'

She stared at him.

'Dr Schofield was the pathologist at the accident last night. I think he is performing the post-mortem this morning. Probably why he can't attend your court.'

'No excuse, he needs to prioritise his work. An inquiry into the circumstances surrounding a man's death should come first.'

Ridpath was tempted to say that given half the police, the mayor of Manchester and a herd of rabid reporters were chasing him, Dr Schofield had probably got his priorities right this time. However, he had the sense to stay silent.

'I wouldn't mind but it was me who recommended him for the job in the first place.'

'To replace Harold Lardner?' The face of the man dubbed the Beast of Manchester flashed into Ridpath's mind. He was the pathologist who committed at least ten violent attacks on women, covering them up by finding people to blame and hiding or changing vital evidence. A murderer in plain sight is always the most difficult to find.

Mrs Challinor stopped and took a deep breath. It was the most agitated Ridpath had ever seen her. Normally she was the epitome of calm control.

'Let's take advantage of this screw up.' She took a file from the top of her desk and handed it to him. 'This is the police investigation into the death of Ronald Wilson. It's not very good work. They even have the temerity to state the man either killed himself or died from accidental drowning. Both radically different explanations of anybody's death. I'd like you to look into it Ridpath.'

'But I have to catch up on all my other work.'

'I think this is important, the police investigation was sloppy.'

'There's another issue. I know the investigating officer.'

'Is that a problem?'

Ridpath shook his head. 'Tommy Harper is overly fond of his beer, but I've always known him to be a diligent investigator.'

'When was the last time you worked with him?'

Ridpath thought back. 'Eight years ago. We were both detective constables working on a serial rapist operating in the university district.'

'Did you catch the man?'

'Yes, more by luck than any great investigation. He was stupid enough to leave his DNA at the scene of the crime. Me and Tommy were on the same investigating team.'

'Follow this case up anyway. We have a week before I have to reopen the inquest.'

'I'm going to the post-mortem on last night's victim, do you want me to talk to Dr Schofield?'

'No, I'll handle it myself. He needs to understand the importance of priorities.'

Her mouth was set and her jaw clenched. Ridpath wouldn't like to annoy Mrs Challinor. He wasn't sure if he would live to tell the tale.

# Chapter Thirteen

Chief Superintendent Trent and Chief Inspector Whitworth were already sitting in the reception area when Ridpath arrived.

'Look what the cat's dragged in,' said Charlie.

'Before you ask, I'm here representing the coroner.'

'Does Margaret Challinor know?' asked Claire Trent.

'You've met her?'

'We're part of the same Legal Women's Group.'

Ridpath had heard of it. Many of the senior female officers in the police were members. Amongst the more chauvinist coppers it was known as the Muffia. He didn't know Margaret Challinor was a member too.

A mortuary assistant appeared in the doorway. 'Dr Schofield will see you now.'

'Makes it sound like we're the ones being examined not the bloody corpse,' said Charlie under his breath.

They walked into an anteroom before the mortuary.

'Dr Schofield would like you to wear these.' She pointed to a set of whites laid out neatly on a table.

'The previous pathologist never bothered asking us to wear this stuff.'

The assistant merely shrugged her shoulders.

That pathologist, Harold Lardner, was now on remand in Wakefield Prison, charged with murder. Ridpath and Charlie Whitworth had been involved in his capture after discovering he had been hiding his victims at a body farm near Preston. Ridpath had heard through the grapevine that he was claiming the murders were caused by the long-term effects of PTSD after being involved in more than 12,000 post-mortems in his time working in Manchester. Whatever the defence, there was no way he was getting off.

'Put them on, Charlie,' ordered Claire Trent.

Reluctantly Charlie started pulling the white overalls over his jacket and trousers. Ridpath and the super followed suit. Claire Trent's outfit was far too big for her.

'Sorry, it's the only size we have,' the assistant apologised.

They walked through into the examination room. Dr Schofield had already started the post-mortem, helped by a male technician. He was speaking loudly so the microphone above his head could record his notes.

'Head: AIS 9. Face, right side: AIS 6. Left side, AIS 4. Neck: AIS 6. Thorax: AIS 6.' Without looking up he paused the recording and said, 'I'll be with you in a moment, just let me finish this gross examination.'

'Certainly looks gross,' said Charlie Whitworth in a loud voice.

The detectives fanned out around the post-mortem table. Ridpath stared at the bright white lights shining down on the body, making it seem even whiter than he remembered. The young man's eyes had been closed but the limbs were still bent at strange angles, like a marionette which had been dropped on the floor. The wound on the head had already been cleaned, revealing a deep gash with the serrated bone edge of the skull clearly visible. The angel had vanished now to be replaced by the open cavity of the man's chest where the pathologist had folded back the two sides of the Y section.

In his early years as a detective Ridpath had been known as "Vomit Man" for his reaction to a post-mortem. But not anymore. Now they just left him cold, a chill that seemed to swamp his body, penetrating deep into the bones. The only reaction these days was a desperate desire for a cigarette after it had all finished. A sort of post-mortem need to rid his nose, mouth and lungs of the stench and taste of death.

The doctor carried on speaking. '…AIS Upper Extremity: right side AIS 6, left side, AIS 3. Lower Extremity: AIS 6, both sides. The ISS is 75.' Finally, he stopped examining the corpse and turned towards them. 'Welcome to my world, detectives. I would ask you don't talk when the microphone is switched on, it screws up my notes. If you would like to ask a question, put up your hand and I will answer you.'

Charlie Whitworth raised his arm. 'What was all that about?'

Dr Schofield coughed once and explained slowly as if he were speaking to a child. 'AIS stand for Abbreviated Injury Scale. It's a system of coding to classify and describe the severity of injuries in motor accidents. It represents a threat to life rather than a comprehensive assessment of the injury. This man displays many injuries over AIS 6 indicating the incident was un-survivable. I won't bore you with the maths but his Injury Severity Score was over 75, meaning A&E wouldn't have bothered to work on him. I have written several papers on the subject for the Association for the Advancement of Automotive Medicine,' he said proudly.

'We're all numbers now, are we doctor?'

'And letters. It's Detective…?'

'DI Ridpath, attached to the Coroner's Office.'

'You were there last night weren't you?'

'I was the one who called it in.'

Claire Trent looked at her watch. 'Can we get a move on? I have a management meeting at two p.m.'

The doctor stared at her for a moment before continuing. 'As I was saying, his ISS of over 75 means the injuries were fatal. In layman's terms, this man's suffered a polytrauma. More bones were fractured rather than remain whole, with particular damage being seen on the skull, the pelvic region, the fibula and the tibia. His death was probably instantaneous.'

'Of course, he died straight away, he was hit by a bloody big truck.' Charlie Whitworth laughed, nudging Ridpath with his arm.

'I'll thank you to treat our customers with respect, DCI Whitworth. If you can't, I suggest you leave my post-mortem.'

Charlie Whitworth sighed and said in an audible voice. 'First time I've been told off by a kid in a mortuary.'

'I heard, DCI Whitworth. You may be interested to hear I suffer from Kallmann syndrome, congenital hypogonadotropic hypogonadism to the educated. It's a disease stopping a person from starting or fully completing puberty. It affects both men and women and can leave a person with a youthful appearance, while being adult or above normal adult height. I diagnosed myself when I was seventeen but it took another two years to convince doctors. I attended university still looking about fourteen years old. The good news is I never have to shave. The bad news is my sense of smell is severely diminished and I have a particularly short middle finger.' He held up his hands, still holding a scalpel. 'Happy now you understand why I look as I do?'

Charlie Whitworth stayed silent. Ridpath liked this doctor, he had balls. They may not have dropped yet but he still had them.

Claire Trent glanced at her watch again.

'Shall we continue?' Without waiting for an answer, he clicked on the microphone. 'The man is a young male, approximately nineteen years of age, no ID possible at present. One large tattoo of a pair of angel wings on his upper chest extending to the ribs, no other tattoos on the body.'

'Was he a druggie?'

The pathologist sighed. Without switching off the microphone he answered DCI Whitworth. 'I am still waiting for the toxicology results to come back from the lab, but there are no indications of needle use nor are there any other signs of prolonged drug use. The young man appears fit, healthy and in the prime of life. Any other questions? Let's get them over and done with now, shall we?'

'Dental work?' asked Ridpath.

'Pretty standard National Health – a few fillings and no extractions. Wisdom teeth not yet descended.'

'What about congenital health problems?'

'A good question Detective Superintendent Trent – but I'm afraid nothing. The heart, liver and kidneys are all functioning perfectly. Shame this man didn't have a donor card on him, he could have saved at least three lives. Shame the law hasn't changed already.' The assistant wiped the sweat of his brow. 'Anything else?'

They all shook their heads.

'Perhaps you will allow me to tell you what *is* of interest. See here. He picked up a small camera and focused it on a mark on the upper left arm. The picture appeared on the screen of a round brown partially healed mark on the left upper arm. 'And here. And here. And here.'

'What are they?' asked Claire Trent, 'marks from the accident?'

'I don't think so. They are partially healed so must have occurred before the event. But I've sent samples off to the lab.'

'So what do you think they are?' asked Charlie, impatiently.'

'I'm not in the habit of speculating, DCI Whitworth, but to me they look like cigarette burns. The lab will let us know when they have completed their analysis.'

'Are they self-inflicted?'

'Again, I don't know, DI Ridpath. Gentlemen... and lady, you are asking me to have an opinion before I have analysed the evidence. It's like asking a *Strictly* judge to give a mark before they have seen the competitors dance.'

'I didn't know you watched *Strictly Come Dancing*, doctor,' said Claire Trent.

'I don't. It was a simile to help you understand. Now if I can continue?'

The watching detectives all nodded their heads.

'That's not all.' He moved the camera up to the victim's mouth. 'Unfortunately the right hand side is too damaged to provide any evidence, but the left displays tears and abrasions in the corner of the mouth. We have taken swabs looking for fibres but I'm not too hopeful.' Again the camera moved, this time to the right wrist. 'More abrasions here above the wrists. Unfortunately, there has been damage during the accident so I can't make out what may have caused them. The lab should be able to tell us more. There is bruising on the underside of the hands...'

'When did he get those marks, Dr Schofield?' asked Claire Trent.

'Within a day or so of his death, Detective Superintendent. The bruises have healed but not a great deal.'

'So they were inflicted before he died?'

'Definitely. Finally, there is a small amount of residue under the fingernails. I've also sent this to the lab for analysis.' The doctor stared at the body lying on the slab. 'This person has been through far too much for evidence to remain on the skin.' He shook his shoulders as waking himself up.

'Are the abrasions rope burns, doctor?' asked Ridpath.

A long, audible sigh. 'I don't indulge in guesswork. We will wait for the lab to come back to me and then I will complete my report. I am a scientist, DI Ridpath. My job is to tell you what I discover, not to solve the case nor to indulge my imagination.'

There was a silence for a moment before Claire Trent looked at her watch and said. 'Thank you Dr Schofield.'

The doctor held up his hand. It was still holding a scalpel. 'I will tell you, however, these other injuries were not as a result of the accident. They occurred well before the incident on the motorway.'

## Chapter Fourteen

They all stood outside the mortuary smoking cigarettes. Opposite, Manchester Royal Infirmary bustled with activity. Doctors in white coats walked by, studiously avoiding the small group on the pavement.

Ridpath knew he shouldn't have accepted one of Claire Trent's Sobranies but once it was offered he couldn't turn it down. Charlie Whitworth, however, had no such qualms. He made it clear he enjoyed his red Embassy far too much to ever give them up.

Ridpath felt a bit of an idiot holding the long, black and gold tipped cigarette between his fingers, but once the cool smoke had snaked into his lungs, he enjoyed the soothing jolt of a particularly good tobacco.

Charlie took a long drag on his cigarette, expelling the blue smoke into the air above his head, where it formed a small cloud before drifting off to join the lead, carbon dioxide and carbon monoxide comprising the breathable air of Manchester.

'First time, I've ever been told off by a kid,' said Charlie between puffs of tobacco.

'Didn't you hear a word he said,' Trent sneered, 'the man suffers from Kallmann syndrome.'

'What's that when it's at home?'

'You didn't hear anything did you?'

Charlie shrugged his shoulders.

'He's had delayed puberty. My bet he's still taking hormone therapy to balance his lack of testosterone.'

The DCI chuckled. 'So he's got no balls.'

'Oh, I think he has plenty of balls, Charlie. Look at the way he handled you.'

Ridpath decided to interrupt this love fest between his two senior officers. 'The marks on the victim are classic signs of someone being tied up.'

'How do you jump to that conclusion?' challenged Claire Trent.

'Abrasions on the wrists, tears around the mouth...'

'Where's your evidence? He could have cut himself shaving for all we know.'

'He was scared and running from someone. Perhaps he'd been tied up and escaped.'

'So you're still peddling this tripe about a man with a gun. A man who nobody else saw and who didn't appear on any CCTV?' Charlie Whitworth was as aggressive as he was with any witness. Claire Trent was just staring at him.

'I know what I saw. And what about the other marks on his arms?'

Charlie Whitworth's eyes rolled. 'They could be from anything. His work, a sport he plays, he may even have a rough girlfriend.'

Ridpath glanced across at Claire Trent, who was examining something on the ground with the point of her shoe.

'I know what I saw, Charlie. He was...'

'Boys, boys,' she held up her hands. 'I have the mayor, the chief constable and half the press in England breathing down my neck because we managed to jam up Manchester's traffic for four hours before a major football match on a Wednesday night.'

'I...' Ridpath began to speak but she held up her hand stopping him instantly.

'We've heard enough from you, DI Ridpath. I still think our best theory is he was a druggie who was off his head and decided to take a jog across the M60 for some unknown reason. And that's what I'll be telling the chief constable when I meet him in...' she checked her Patek Philippe watch, '...twenty-seven minutes. At the moment we don't know who our victim is. We know nothing about him, his lifestyle or habits. Our new pathologist will report back in a day or two.' She smiled like a hyena seeing a goat tied to a post. 'So Charlie, in the meantime you need to show me how good you are. Your most important job is to find out who our unknown vic is. Give a kick up the arse to fingerprints. With a bit of luck he's already on the database. And get on to toxicology. I want the report on my desk asap, yesterday if possible.' She gave a slight wave of her hand.

A hundred yards away a car engine started and raced forward.

'You've forgotten one thing, guvnor. What about the car next to me on the M60, the one with false number plates. Shouldn't we be looking for it?' asked Ridpath.

The BMW accelerated to a stop at the kerb. A young DC jumped out of the car and opened the rear door.

'The other car? Give it the attention it deserves.' As Claire Trent stepped into the car, she turned back and said, 'Pull your finger out, Charlie. I can keep the bastards away from this one for a day or so, but I want results. And quickly.'

'What do you want me to do?'

The steel-blue eyes turned on Ridpath. 'You? Don't you think you've done enough? For the moment, you're assigned to the Coroner's Office. I suggest you do your job there. Margaret Challinor doesn't suffer fools gladly.'

The door slammed shut and the car raced off.

'Up yours, ma'am,' said Charlie under his breath.

# Chapter Fifteen

The two detectives were left standing on the pavement.

'You believe me, don't you Charlie?'

'I believe the evidence and so far you are the only witness who reports seeing a man with a gun at the side of the motorway. No CCTV or dash cams support you.'

'Why would I make something like that up?'

The DCI shrugged his shoulders and took another long drag on his cigarette. 'How's the cancer?'

Ridpath eyed his boss suspiciously, 'In remission,' he said quietly.

'You still taking pills?'

'I see where you're going with this. "Hallucinations as a result of taking tablets for his illness, your honour".' Ridpath mimicked Charlie's demeanour when giving evidence in court. 'They are not "pills". It's Revlimid. Just one a day, no side effects.'

For a second his mind flashed back to the awful day he had to tell Polly he had cancer. Watching her face as the news sank home and then the inevitable question.

'Are you going to die?'

'Not if I can help it, I want to see Eve grow up. The consultant says there's a new course of treatment which, if I start straight away, gives me the possibility of remission.'

Of course Polly spent the next two hours researching myeloma.

'It says here the prognosis is you have four years to live… at most.' She looked at him with her eyes filled with tears. 'Four years, Ridpath, that's all you have.'

'The consultant explained it to me. It was before they discovered this new combination treatment. Their success rate is much higher now, many people go into remission and the cancer disappears.'

He could hear the words now, only half believing them, but trying to keep a brave face for Polly.

It was funny but he knew the strongest person at that moment had to be the one whose health was the weakest. So it goes.

Then followed the course of treatment. Christies were brilliant but nobody should have ever to go through what he faced.

He was put on an experimental treatment of a combination of Revlimid, cyclophosphamide, and dexamethasone, called RCD by the consultant, all of which were taken by mouth in twenty-eight-day cycles. The cyclophosphamide was the chemotherapy, while the 'D' element was a steroid. Some days he had to take more than thirty-two tablets.

He had four cycles and then went on to stem cell collection; more days visiting the hospital, more injections and long hours sitting with a needle in his right arm and another in his left, connected by tubing to a machine that took stem cells out of his blood and then returned the blood back to his body.

It felt like something from a 1930s Frankenstein movie with him as the re-created monster.

Then came the killer time when they gave him high doses of melphalan to kill off the cancer cells and reintroduce his own stem cells. Four weeks in total isolation at Christies, unable to touch or hold Polly and Eve. A bastard of a time, not knowing if the treatment would work.

He couldn't face it again.

Not again.

'…Ridpath…'

He heard his name being spoken.

'You'd been driving back from Teesside. How long is the journey? Four, five hours? Did you take a rest?'

Ridpath shook his head. 'I was in a hurry to get back.'

'The blood alcohol test is going to come back clean, isn't it?'

It was Ridpath's turn to roll his eyes. 'Of course, it is. The last time I had a drink was the night before, at the end of course party.'

'You were tired. It had been two weeks of hard work on the course. You're taking drugs for cancer. It all happened in a flash. You thought you saw a man with a gun at the side of the road...'

'That's bollocks, Charlie.'

The DCI took the last drag on his Embassy before flicking it into the gutter. 'Listen, you know how it works. You can't bring a whole city to a stop without somebody taking the blame. Our glorious leader is sitting in the back of her car working out whether to give you up now or wait until the toxicology comes back with evidence of cocaine, speed or E in the victim's body.'

'She wouldn't do anything like that.'

'Wanna bet?' Charlie's arm came round Ridpath's shoulders. 'That's what I always liked about you, Ridpath. Your bloody naivety. You still think it's all about just doing the job and putting the bad guys away. Well, listen to your Uncle Charlie. Look what happened to John Gorman. Best bloody copper I ever worked with. Makes one mistake and they throw him to the wolves.'

'He retired on a full pension, Charlie.'

'Aye, with at least six good years of work still left in him. You know what the best bloody detective in Manchester is doing at the moment?'

'I'm sure you're going to tell me.'

'He's growing rhubarb on his allotment. Bloody rhubarb.' The DCI's eyes narrowed as he shoved his face even closer to

Ridpath's. 'And I haven't forgotten, it was you and that bloody woman, Margaret Challinor, who helped end his career.'

Ridpath pushed him away.

Charlie started to laugh. 'What do the foreigners call it? Karma, that's it. Well, your bloody karma's just come and shat on your head, Ridpath. You're stuffed.'

He turned and walked back to the car park, laughing and shaking his head.

Ridpath stood there for a moment. An ambulance drove past heading for A&E, its siren blaring and lights flashing.

He reached into his pocket for his car keys.

Shit.

The car was still being held by the forensic team.

Could the day get worse?

# Chapter Sixteen

'You're very tense.' She dug her nails deeper into his shoulder muscles, feeling him respond to the pressure of her massage. 'Just relax. It's all been planned to the last detail.'

'I just don't like you being with him. He's scum, they all are.'

She dug her nails in deeper feeling him flinch. 'Don't worry, it won't be for long. It will make it easier for you. A naked man has nowhere to hide.'

He smirked. 'Or nothing to hide.'

'You're to wait until I go to the bathroom, understand? And have the tranquilliser ready. I'll make sure he drinks the GHB, but we need to have him more compliant. A heavy dose of Ambien should do the trick.'

'Are you sure you can get him to come back to the house?'

She let go of his shoulders, pushing back the rough material of his sweat shirt to cover his muscles. 'By the time I've finishing teasing him, he'll be like a dog on heat.' She tapped his head. 'Men, you should think more with this and less with these.' She grabbed his balls.

He shied away covering himself. 'And afterwards?' he asked quickly.

'We hold him but not for long this time. We need to ratchet up the pressure. The sooner they start blaming each other the better.'

'His father will go apeshit...'

'The favourite son and appointed heir shot dead, and his dick cut off. If that doesn't set him off, nothing will.'

'I still don't like the dumping ground. It's too open, what if we're spotted on CCTV?'

'I've already fixed the cameras at the church; it'll take them years to put them right. And hiding in plain sight is our strength. There will be so many cars in the area shopping on a Saturday ours will be difficult to spot.'

'I still don't know.'

She walked up to him and put her arms around his neck. 'Listen brother, have I been wrong so far?'

He didn't say anything.

'You just do what I tell you. We've started it now, we carry on to the end.'

'Don't you feel anything for the people we're going to kill?'

She shook her head. 'Not a thing. They are just corpses in my way. You're not going soft on me like Ronnie, are you?'

Her brother shook his head.

'Look, we had to get rid of him. He was going to tell the police what we were doing. It was the right thing to do.'

'I know, I just...'

'You just need to be focused, brother. It's what our father would have wanted. We're doing this for him. Nothing else matters.'

# Chapter Seventeen

Ridpath parked on the hard shoulder of the M60 with his warning lights flashing.

He knew the accident had happened somewhere near here, but nothing marked the spot. Not even a bloody big X. No police sign asking for witnesses to come forward. No chalk outline of a body in the middle of the road. No orange and white tape on any of the barriers.

It was as if the accident had never happened.

He had picked up his car from the forensic garage, finding it covered in a fine white powder. They had even dusted his dashboard. At least they had been thorough.

He had sat behind the wheel in the garage for a long time, thinking what to do. He knew he couldn't just go home. The place would be quiet and empty, with only the warmth of a bottle of Laphroaig waiting for him. He could go back to the coroner's office in Stockfield to catch up on the cases he had missed. But the only person likely to be there was Mrs Challinor and he didn't want to see her just yet.

It was obvious to him neither Charlie Whitworth nor Claire Trent were going to fight his corner. If there was going to be a sacrificial lamb for last night's gridlock it was going to be him. That was certain.

He lit a cigarette he found in the glove compartment, enjoying the way the smoke filled the interior of the car, replacing the smell of fingerprint powder with the sweet tang of tobacco. He took a long drag and coughed. Stale tobacco.

For a second he was taken back to the first time he had smoked – in the outside Jacks at school, along with Tony Hughes and Dermot Callaghan. It seemed so long ago now. All three of them sardined together in the toilet with the broken door, swallowing the bitter smoke from the Park Drive Dermot had stolen from his father. A few quick, shared puffs and they were real men, just like the workers in Trafford Park. The aroma of the Jacks would stay with him forever: A sweet combination of piss, sodden paper and fungus-stained water that ran down the walls and pooled between their legs.

He liked the lessons at Xaverian well enough, but the Dominican Father who taught them was a foul tempered old man with a halo of sweat clinging to him like a shroud. Ginger hair sprouted from his knuckles and nose like orange weed. A rope tied around his waist, yellow with age and sweat and rust, held his body together like a sack of Irish potatoes.

Catholic schooldays. He was sure it was the same the world over. He was no longer a Catholic though, the Fathers had beat any belief in God out of him. The arrival of the myeloma when he was just thirty-five simply reinforcing his lack of religion. How could any all-powerful God allow it to happen?

Enough wallowing in the past, Ridpath. Unless he did something he was going to be well and truly screwed by a system that put more emphasis on assigning blame than encouraging success.

If he was going to get out of this hole it would be down to himself. Not Charlie bloody Whitworth or Claire Trent.

So here he was parked on the hard shoulder of the M60, risking life and limb as cars raced past less than five feet away.

He stepped out of the car and looked around. The scene was totally different from yesterday. For one, all the traffic was moving and secondly, there wasn't a massive artic blocking the lanes with a body lying in the middle of the road.

To his left Sale Water Park was quiet and serene. Though the trees he could just spot the huge man-made lake, created fifty years ago by the flooding of a gravel pit. In front of him, the deafening noise of traffic racing to its destination like blood corpuscles hurrying to a site of infection. Each one holding just one staring driver in his metal box.

He walked back towards where he thought the accident had happened, looking at the middle of the road.

Nothing.

He stopped once more to get his bearings. There was the tall yellow tower with the camera pointing directly at him. He gave whoever was watching a wave and carried on. From what he remembered, it should be a little further back.

And then he saw it. A small dark patch in the middle lane about a foot square, looking like an accidental oil spill. It was all that remained of the victim's blood. A small memorial to a life lost.

He walked on, seeing the black skid marks of his tyres etched into the road surface. Had the traffic cops measured the length to check how fast he had been going?

Probably.

Next to them were large tyre marks in the outside lane. But they were much shorter. Obviously, the lorry driver had seen the victim far too late to stop in time. The tyre tracks thickened and then continued on past what was left of the victim's blood.

Nothing marked the spot where the accident had taken place.

Just cars racing past, rushing to go shopping, dashing to the football, or simply hurrying to see their family. The thought made him stop for a moment. He hadn't called Eve to apologise yet for yesterday. He knew he was putting it off but he couldn't face her voice. She would never accuse him of not caring about her but he would hear the tears in her speech. A dubious pleasure he would save for later.

He tried to force his mind back to that fateful moment less than twenty-four hours ago. The man running from the left, braking suddenly, looking back to the man with the gun, standing behind the crash barrier. Standing behind, not on the hard shoulder.

Behind the crash barrier.

He looked over to the left.

A six-foot high wooden fence separated the Water Park from the motorway.

Had the young man somehow managed to climb over it?

In his imagination, he tried to remember the angle of the man's run. It was to the left and behind where he was standing. He stepped over the knee-high metal barrier, down a small ditch in the grass and strode over to the fence.

It seemed solid enough; overlapping panels of pine dowsed in creosote. The panels were set in a concrete foundation running along the bottom. Unusually for Manchester there were very few pieces of graffiti. Denis Wuz Here, City Champs, Wythenshawe Forever, and Bogside Boys.

The last was a beautifully decorated double B logo which Ridpath recognised as a gang mark. Like lions' spray marking their territory. In Manchester's case it was done with spray paint rather than urine. But from the smell they may have pissed here too.

He walked along the fence checking it. About twenty yards along he noticed three of the panels gave slightly as he pushed them. He stopped and pushed harder.

Nothing happened except for a slight give in the fence. He stepped back. From the front it looked the same as every other part of the fence but as he went closer he saw the three panels were not joined to the rest. He pushed them aside with his hand and they slid to the side like a door.

He popped his head through the gap and looked around. The land sloped down from the fence through a gap in the trees to a road wending its way through the Water Park.

Had the young man run this way? Did he know about the door in the fence? Was the man with the gun chasing after him? Had he just stepped through when Ridpath saw him?

Ridpath eased his body through the door, careful not to touch the sides. The dirt path was clearer now, a definite gap between the trees.

At the bottom a teenager in a hoodie was just walking from the road onto the path heading towards Ridpath, his head down, hands in his pocket, kicking gravel in front of him.

'Oi, you!' Ridpath shouted.

The lad looked up suddenly, saw Ridpath shouting at him, turned in a heartbeat and ran back the way he had come.

Ridpath shouted again. 'You. Stop. Police.'

The lad kept running.

'Stop, you little bugger.'

Ridpath threw himself down the trail, feeling his feet slip and slide on the greasy soil. His legs went from under him and he was flat on his back, still sliding down the trail. He came to a halt in a tangle of undergrowth and soil litter.

Throwing the branches off him, he got up and raced down the trail, taking more care this time and slowing whenever it became too steep.

He reached the place where he had seen the lad and looked right and left.

Nothing.

On the left a couple of old Victorian houses, one displaying a sign for a cats' and dogs' home. On the right more trees on either side of the path, leading to the artificial lake.

But he couldn't see the boy. It was like he had vanished into thin air. Manchester's own Houdini. Where did he come from? Where was he going to?

Ridpath trudged back up the trail, brushing off the dirt and leaves from the jacket and trousers of his suit. Another bloody bill, this time for dry-cleaning.

He reached the top close to the fence and turned to look again. Obviously, this route was used as a short cut between estates. He could imagine the boys taking their life in their hands every time they crossed the M60, gloating in their bravado.

He stepped through the fence and heard the loud whoop of a siren in front of him. Parked behind his car was a police BMW with a tall copper stepping out of it, placing his cap on his head.

Ridpath ran back to the motorway.

The copper checked him. 'Is this car, yours, sir?'

'I can...'

'Licence and registration, please.'

'Look, I can explain...'

'Licence and registration first, explanations later.'

'Ridpath pulled out his licence and his warrant card from his wallet. 'I'm on the job, investigating the accident that happened here yesterday.'

The copper looked at him dubiously. 'On your own, are you?'

'Just digging around. There was a hole in the fence over there, I...'

As Ridpath was speaking, the copper's eyes suddenly widened. 'I recognise you. You're the idiot who thought they saw a man with a gun yesterday. Shut the road down.'

'I am Detective Inspector Ridpath and I'll thank you to treat me with respect, constable.'

The traffic cop's radio squawked and he turned away to answer it. 'Go ahead, control. The car belongs to a Detective Inspector Ridpath. He claims to be investigating the accident yesterday.'

'I *am* looking into it.'

The constable nodded. 'Roger that.' He turned back to face Ridpath. 'That was my boss. Apparently, you two met yesterday. He's told me to say that it is an offence to be parked illegally on a motorway. You will remove your car immediately...'

'But I'm working on a case.'

'According to my boss, there is no log in the book telling us MIT are investigating in this area.' The man's voice softened. 'Sorry, but he's told me to give you a ticket. The fine is eighty quid. You could get your guvnor to ring him but Harry Todd is pretty pissed off with you.'

Ridpath sighed and waved his hand. 'Just give me the bloody ticket.'

Somehow, the day had got worse.

## Chapter Eighteen

After the run in with Traffic, he decided he would cut his losses and return home. He could go in at the weekend and catch up on work. Besides, he had a phone call to make.

It took him twenty minutes and two cups of strong coffee before he finally plucked up the courage to make the call. 'Hi there, sweetpea.'

Silence on the other end of the phone.

'Look, I'm really sorry about yesterday. Daddy had a few problems at work.'

A snuffle. 'We were supposed to go to see *Coco*. Mummy was going to come too.'

'I know I'm sorry, I had problems at work, sweetpea.'

'I'm not your sweetpea. I'm a grown girl. I'm nearly ten.'

'We can go to see it tomorrow if you like?'

'Yesterday was the last day. And they had free popcorn too.'

'What if I can find it at another cinema. Can we go together?'

'Can Mummy come too?'

'Of course she can. Let me check the Internet and I'll let you both know.'

'Ok, the girls at school say it's great. The music is *soooo* good.'

'Great, I'll find it and let Mummy know.'

A long silence on the end of the phone. 'When are we going to be together, Daddy?'

'As soon as I find out where the film is playing...'

'No, I meant forever, like it used to be. I'm sick of eating rice and Grandma won't let me eat pizza or watch my iPad.'

The explanation Ridpath had been dreading. 'Sometimes, adults go through problems. Me and Mummy are trying to work them out so we can be together again. OK?'

'Like when I fell out with Harriet Butler about BTS?'

'BTS?'

'A Korean boy band. They're so dreamy, Young Oh has these lovely eyes…'

'Kind of like that, but different, if you know what I mean?'

'I guess so.'

'Can I speak to Mummy?'

'Ok, she's right next to me.'

'But before you give her the phone, are you still my sweetpea?'

A quiet, 'Yes.'

'And remember, I'll always love you, sweetpea, even when hell freezes over…'

'…On a summer's day in Manchester.' She finished his sentence for him. It was their secret joke about the weather. Something nobody else, including his wife, understood. 'Here she is.'

'Hello, Ridpath. At least you made the call.'

'Sorry about yesterday.'

'I suppose it was work again.'

'Don't be like that, Polly. You know what it's like.'

'I know you seem to put your job ahead of your daughter or me. When are you going to learn it's just a job, Ridpath? You're not saving the world.'

Polly had been his rock when he had been going through his treatment and the recovery that followed. But somehow over the nine months their relationship had changed. She had blamed the job for his illness; the stress, long, antisocial hours, the sheer pressure of being at the blunt end of a system that paid little attention to human frailty.

Sometime during the nine months he had been ill she had stopped being a wife and a lover, becoming instead a mother.

A role they both hated yet neither could halt. He didn't blame her, it was just he wished she didn't try to wrap him in cotton wool all the time. But he still loved her and always would. Did she feel the same way about him though?

'If I can find the movie...'

'*Coco.*'

'That was it. If I can find *Coco* on at another cinema tomorrow, will you come?'

A pause. 'Possibly.'

'Is that a yes or a no?'

'It's a possibly.'

'It would make Eve happy.'

'Don't use Eve against me, Ridpath,' she snapped.

'I'm not, it's just... well... it would be nice to go out together again.'

'I have an appointment tomorrow. I'm dyeing my hair.' When they had first met, Polly's black Chinese hair had been dyed a dark green. For some obscure reason it was something that attracted Ridpath to her all those years ago. The rebel who didn't take anything, even her looks, too seriously.

Ridpath laughed. 'Really?'

'Really.'

'What colour this time?'

'I thought a fetching shade of mauve.'

'What will the school say?'

'Bugger the school. I'm a teacher not a paragon of virtue.'

'You could set a trend. Mauve-haired eight-year-olds.'

'Mrs Rogers would have kittens.'

'When are you doing it?'

'The appointment's at 3:30 p.m.'

'So you'll be finished by six?'

'Possibly.'

'I'll book the cinema after then. Three seats...' He crossed his fingers.

'OK, but not too late. Eve has ballet on Saturday morning.'

'OK, see you tomorrow. I'll message with the time.'

Another pause. 'Have you been to see Christies yet?

'The appointment is at lunchtime tomorrow. The usual check-up and meeting with the vampire.'

'She still can't find your veins?'

'Takes three stabs and still misses. Eventually she gets it right and the blue stuff comes pouring out of me.'

Once a month he had to have his blood checked at the famous cancer hospital. It was a time he hated. Waiting for the phone call that told him either he was still in remission or the cancer had returned. It was like waiting for the hangman to release the trapdoor.

'You didn't tell me what the last results were.'

'And you didn't ask.' As soon as the words left his mouth, Ridpath regretted them.

'I'm not your bloody mother. I shouldn't have to ask.'

'No, sorry, I should have told you.'

'And?'

'All clear. As fit as a butcher's dog.'

'That's good news. Wrap up well before you go, Ridpath. Jesus Christ, I can't believe I'm mothering you again, as if looking after thirty kids in school every day isn't enough...'

And a loud buzz echoed in Ridpath's ear. She had cut the line.

Ridpath thought about calling her back, but the detective in him knew that now was not the right time.

## Chapter Nineteen

Charlie Whitworth felt tired. His world had changed in the last couple of weeks. He had gone from being in the running to head MIT with a lovely promotion on the side to being constantly on the run from a new boss.

Even worse, she was a woman.

Now he had nothing against women. Some of them make excellent officers, especially in the support roles. Look at Chrissy Wright, bright, diligent and hard-working, he didn't know what he would do without her.

However, if he was faced with a gang of armed drug dealers he knew he would prefer a Dave Hardy by his side armed with a weighted cosh, rather than a female detective armed with a leather handbag.

He knew it wasn't a fashionable view but he wasn't a very fashionable man. He had worked all the hours God gave him to provide for his family and look what had happened. The wife hardly spoke to him any more, spending most of her time sleeping. And the kids? Well one was studying sociology in university. The last time they met, they had a big argument.

'Look Dad, when society is unequal, deviant behaviour is to be expected. It's the rebellion of the poor and disenfranchised against the norms of a society that has labelled them unfit.'

'Bollocks. They are thugs and drug dealers whose one idea in life is to make a lot of money from the misfortune of others.'

'How many people have you arrested for drugs in your career?'

Charlie smiled. 'I've lost count there's been so many.'

'And has it made a blind bit of difference? If anything, drugs are now more prevalent and available than they ever were. Have twenty-odd years of your life made any difference?'

He hadn't answered her. There was no point. She was questioning the whole meaning of his life.

They had spent the next twenty minutes avoiding the subject before she said she had to go. 'John's coming round.'

'Your lecturer boyfriend? I thought he was married? And isn't there a university policy against relationships between teachers and pupils.'

She stood up. 'Sometimes Dad, you can be a real pig.'

She'd slung her bag over her shoulder and flounced out of the cafe.

They hadn't spoken since that chat three weeks ago. He'd call her this weekend. She would have forgiven him by now.

He wouldn't take it back though. It wasn't right. She was just a girl being taken advantage of by an older man. Perhaps he should call university security and make a complaint. Or even better, write an anonymous letter to the vice-chancellor. That would cook the lecherous lecturer's goose.

There was a knock on his door.

'Enter.'

Dave Hardy popped his head in. 'You got a minute, guvnor?'

'Come in, Dave, I'm just trying to get my head around the world. Where did we go wrong, Dave?'

'I don't know what you mean? Did we go wrong?'

Charlie Whitworth waved a hand in front of his face, dismissing the question. 'Never mind. What can I do for you?'

'It's about the job, Charlie. It's like this, I'm up for early retirement in a few years and well, the missus is pushing me to take it and get a more regular job until then.'

'You want out of MIT?'

'It's not so much that. It's more of looking after myself in the next couple of years, have an easier life. And with all the changes recently, John Gorman going and the new woman coming in, I thought it was a good time to let you know.'

'You'd give up working with MIT on major cases for "an easier life".'

'It's just a job, Charlie.'

'Just a job! It's far more than that, but if your head is in that place maybe it is time for you to go. There'll be a queue of eager young detectives waiting to take your seat out there.'

Dave Hardy held up his hand. 'I am sorry, boss, I just think it's the right time to make a move. I mean I don't want to end up like Ridpath.'

'Ridpath's a good officer.'

'A good officer who had cancer and now his wife has left him and he still can't see further than the job. Last night, he closed the bloody M60. I don't want to end up like him.'

'Or me?'

Dave Hardy didn't answer.

'Your mind is made up?

'It is, boss,'

'Fine, I'll start looking for a cushy number for you. In the meantime, you can do something for me. Our new boss needs taking down a peg or two...'

# Chapter Twenty

He had his arm round the young woman's body, touching her breast from the side. Her head was resting on his shoulder, her eyes closed.

He could see the taxi driver's eyes looking at them through his rear mirror. She had been so keen on tonight's date, she had even picked him up. This one was gagging for it.

'Keep your eyes on the road, mate,' he ordered.

'Is she ok?'

Phil Marsland looked down on the sleeping woman leaning on his shoulder. He reached up to stroke her fine blonde hair. He would definitely take pictures of this one. A special one for his album.

'Is she ok?' The taxi driver repeated his question.

'She's fine. Just had one too many. Girls these days…' he snorted, 'can't hold their drink.'

He had helped of course, buying her double gins and tonic instead of singles and encouraging her to neck some tequila shots. Well, you have to help them along, don't you? Otherwise you'd never get your end away. And he wanted this one for his collection badly. A picture of her lying spreadeagled on the bed would be a lovely shot for his mates. Definitely one for the album.

'I wish my wife were like that. It's like pouring water down a well with her. Drinks away all my bloody money.'

'That why you driving one of these?'

The driver nodded, his eyes looking through the rear mirror. 'Got two kids as well, eat me out of house and bloody home.'

'You're bloody young for two kids.'

'Had them when she was seventeen. Had to marry her, didn't I?'

'You should have practised the 4Fs.'

'4Fs?'

'Find 'em. Feel 'em. Fuck 'em. And forget 'em. My dad taught me when I was fourteen. Best advice he ever gave me.'

'Your dad's a bit of lad, is he?'

'You don't wanna know mate.' Phil Marsland smirked. 'You don't wanna know.'

The driver checked his satnav. 'Where is this bloody place anyway? We must be close now.'

Phil Marsland nudged the young woman next to him, using more force than was really necessary. She woke up with a start, her eyes unfocused and her head wobbling on the end of her neck. 'Where am I?'

'We're going home, love. To your home...'

She gazed out of the window, trying to focus. 'Turn left, here.'

The driver turned left into a narrow country lane bordered on either side by hedges.

'Wouldn't think a place like this existed in Manchester.'

'My dad's,' she mumbled. 'Let's me use it when he's not there.'

Phil Marsland smiled. This was looking good. She was taking him back to an empty house. He was definitely going to get his end away, whether she wanted to or not.

She reached out and shakily pointed to a house on the left. 'Here.'

The taxi driver stopped and the young woman opened the door.

'That'll be twenty-five quid, mate. Or do you want me to wait?'

Phil Marsland checked the woman. She was leaning against a fence post trying to steady herself. he reached into his wallet and gave the driver three tenners. 'Nah, we'll be OK. Keep the change, mate.'

He got out of the car. The house was old, standing alone in the middle of this forest. Off to his left he could see the orange glow of the M60, accompanied by the steady drone of traffic. To his right the barks of large dogs from another house about a hundred yards away.

What a strange place, but perfect for what he had in mind.

Nobody was going to hear her screams.

He strode over to her and hooked his arm around her shoulders. 'Take it easy…,' he tried to remember her name. What was her name again? Never mind, he'd ask in the morning. It usually pissed them off when he did, but by then he'd finished with them anyway.

'What you doin'?' She mumbled.

'Helping you into your house.'

'You can't stay here, my dad…'

'I know all about your dad, you told me remember?'

He helped her stagger to the front door.

'Where are your keys?'

She pulled her bag round to her front and fumbled with the catch.

He unfastened it quickly and reached inside to pull out a keychain with a picture of the Virgin Mary.

Wonderful, a God–Squadder. He always liked helping them see the light.

He leant the young woman at the side of the door and hunted for the right key, eventually finding it. The door opened and she slid inside. He caught her before she fell and helped her into the living room.

'You should go now,' she mumbled.

'Can't leave you like this. And anyway, I thought we were going to have a party, just me and you.'

At the word party, she lifted her head and smiled. 'I need a drink.'

'You've had too much already.'

'Just one more and we can go upstairs.'

A bottle of vodka was standing on a table with some glasses and an ice bucket. He splashed a large glassful for himself and a small one for her, adding two cubes of ice to their drinks. The little minx must have been planning for him to come back here tonight. She had everything ready.

He felt her arm go round his waist. She was standing next to him, her head nestling into his shoulder. The glass of vodka was taken from him.

'Let's neck these in one and go upstairs to bed.'

She looked at him with blue eyes and a dirty little smile curling her lips. He knew she was a little minx this one. He downed his drink, feeling the rush of vodka through his body.

She placed her glass back down on the table without drinking it. 'Come on.' She took him by the hand and led him upstairs.

His legs wobbled as they climbed the stairs. The vodka was strong. No worries, once he got to bed everything would be fine. The drink would help him loosen up. She was already as loose as a blow-up doll.

At the top she opened a door and pointed to the bed. Leaning into him, she whispered, 'You get undressed. I'll just go for a pee.'

She pushed him into the bedroom, closing the door.

He felt strange, the bloody vodka was strong. He kicked off his shoes and threw his jacket on the back of the chair. The room was almost empty; a chair, the bed and a bedside table. That was it, looked like nobody lived here. Perhaps she just used this place to shag. One of her dad's perks, an empty house.

He put his mobile phone and wallet on the bedside table. Needed to have the phone handy for when he took the pictures. He would make sure everybody could see her face. And afterwards he could even use them for a little slut shaming. Post them on the net for everyone to see.

He laughed out loud at the thought.

He tried to take off his trousers but he kept falling over. That bloody vodka had a kick to it. Never mind. He sat on the bed and pulled them off with his feet, kicking them to the far wall. He whipped his V-neck over his head and slipped between the covers.

He couldn't wait to shag this one. What would his mates say, sleeping with the enemy?

He chuckled to himself. He would definitely take pictures of her.

The door was opening slowly. Here she was. He couldn't wait to see her naked.

But it wasn't the blonde young woman standing in the doorway. It was the taxi driver and he had a black gun in his hand. What was he doing here?

'Nice to see you again, Phil.'

He was joined by the blonde woman, but she was still fully clothed. What was she doing with all her clothes on?

'Sorry to disappoint you, Phil, but you won't be enjoying my pleasures tonight. Instead, my brother is going to be having some fun with you. I'm afraid you won't enjoy it though.'

Why was she speaking in that way? And why wasn't she drunk anymore?

And what was that about her brother?

Phil Marsland tried to get up from the bed but found he couldn't move. His brain was telling his body to get up but nothing was happening.

The young woman stepped into the bedroom followed by her brother. 'Can you feel the GHB kicking in Phil? Enjoy it while it lasts.'

The taxi driver's fist came crashing into his mouth. The last thing Phil Marsland tasted before he lost consciousness was his own blood.

This wasn't how the night was supposed to end.

# Day Three

*Friday, April 20, 2018*

## Chapter Twenty-One

'It's good to have Ridpath back with us, even if he has decided to come late to our weekly meeting.'

The sarcasm was heavy in Margaret Challinor's voice as he mumbled his apologies and took his seat, placing his latte on the table.

This was the weekly meeting of the Coroner's Office, to check up on outstanding cases, monitor progress and highlight new cases needing investigation. Everybody was in their usual positions; the head coroner at the front, chairing the meeting with the area coroner, Carol Oates, on her left and a part-time coroner from Derbyshire, David Smail, on her right. Jenny sat opposite him taking notes.

'Right, we can get started. How's the Larousse case, Carol?'

'She died of natural causes at home aged seventy-six. The doctor has signed the death cert and it's been countersigned by a colleague. Police were called to the scene, a constable first, then checked by a duty sergeant. All seems in order.'

'When was the last visit by the doctor?'

Carol Oates checked her notepad. Her blonde hair was tightly rolled in an elegant chignon, which complemented her alabaster skin and dark, tailored business suit. As she read, a single hair escaped from its hair grips and long, beautifully manicured fingers gently pressed it back into place. 'Ten days previously. She had been suffering from arthritis for many years. Her medical records are as thick as a telephone book.'

After the Shipman case Mrs Challinor rigorously checked all deaths at home. A murderous doctor was not going to get away with his crimes for thirty years on her watch.

'Good. Next one down is Ronald Wilson. I opened the inquest yesterday but, in the absence of the pathologist's report, I have postponed it for a week.'

Carol Oates turned a page. 'According to my notes the police report was inconclusive. They weren't sure whether it was an accident or suicide. The body was discovered last Thursday, floating in Wingate Lake. Apparently it had been in the water for at least two weeks. Mr Wilson was a twenty-three-year-old male, a couple of arrests for possession but seemed to have turned his life around in the last few years. His absence was reported by his grandmother on April 1. Not the best day to make a missing person's report to the police. They didn't start taking any action for three days afterwards when a neighbour followed up. The investigation looks pretty messy and there's no pathologist's report yet.'

'Any suicide note?' asked Mrs Challinor.

'The police found nothing. And they have yet to find his clothes and wallet. The police think they were probably stolen by local kids.'

'Still haven't found them?' asked Ridpath.

Carol Oates checked the file. 'The report doesn't say. I presume not.'

'Have you read the police report, Ridpath?'

'I have, Mrs Challinor.'

'And?'

'There are a few gaps in the investigation.'

'A few gaps,' Carol Oates said incredulously. She began to count off her elegantly manicured fingers. 'Can't find Ronald Wilson's clothes. Can't find the witness who called it in. Can't find his wallet? Didn't attend the post-mortem. Shall I go on?'

Mrs Challinor frowned. 'The inquest will reopen next Thursday. This one doesn't smell right to me. Can you follow up, Ridpath? Check out the police investigation and urge the pathologist to complete his report. I want a far more definite answer than "maybe it was suicide or maybe it was an accident".'

Ridpath made a note in his book.

'Shall I schedule it before or after the Rashid inquest?' asked Jenny, fluttering her incredibly long fake eyelashes.

'Before. Once we have a better idea of the police investigation and the pathologist has deigned to provide us with a report, it should be pretty straightforward.'

'Is it the new pathologist?' asked Jenny, 'the one that looks like a deranged teenager let loose in a science lab?'

Ridpath coughed. 'Apparently, he has an illness, Kallmann syndrome.'

'So speaks our resident authority on illness,' added Carol Oates, followed by a fake smile that quickly turned into a grimace.

'He's one of the best young pathologists in the country. He suffers from hypergonadism. And, if you care to know, Carol, I personally recommended him,' Mrs Challinor said sharply.

The two women stared at each other until Carol Oates looked away.

'Although after yesterday's performance, or lack of performance, I wonder if I have made the right choice.'

Ridpath broke the tension. 'I'll get right onto it. The Wilson case, I mean.'

'We also have 178 other cases extant at the moment, Ridpath. If you're looking for more work to practise your newly acquired skills during training, you won't be disappointed.'

'I'll get up to speed as quickly as I can.' He coughed. 'But I'm afraid I have to leave by 12:30.'

'Oh?'

'An appointment at Christies.'

Mrs Challinor arched her brow. 'Nothing serious I hope?'

He shook his head. 'Just the normal check-up and blood donation to the hospital. Three pints of Ridpath's best.'

She made a note in her diary. 'Do make sure you get up to speed, Ridpath, I don't want our clients to suffer because you have fallen behind.'

'Of course not Mrs Challinor. I will be "up to speed" as you call it, by Monday.'

'Good. Any objections, Carol, to Ridpath taking over this case?'

'Fine by me, saves me chasing witnesses.' A little smile appeared on her lips. 'But if he's looking into it, he can handle the rest of the case too. Liaison with the family and all the documentation.'

'The family haven't been told?'

'His grandmother identified the body, but the pathologist hasn't released it yet. Too busy, apparently, with another case. An accident.'

She stared directly at Ridpath. Was she mocking him?

'Is this Ridpath's case?'

'I believe so...' Carol Oates said lightly, the smile on her lips broadening.

'I've opened a file, Mrs Challinor, 4367/18,' said Jenny handing over a pink folder.

'Good. As Ridpath is now handling the Wilson case, you can look after this accident.'

Carol Oates' head snapped round. 'But it was Ridpath who reported it.'

'And that's why he should not be involved in the investigation.'

'But, Margaret, I want to stay involved...'

'Don't you think you are already too involved, Ridpath? You are a witness to the accident, you can't also be the investigating officer for the coroner.'

Had she been talking to Claire Trent? Was this a stitch-up to prevent him knowing what was going on? 'But Margaret...'

'I've decided, Ridpath. Carol will handle this case and bring it to inquest. Understood?'

Reluctantly, Ridpath nodded.

'Good, let's move on. We have a lot to cover this morning.'

# Chapter Twenty-Two

After the meeting Ridpath returned to his desk. Jenny had already placed a large stack of files on top of it, all requiring his attention. But before he plunged in, it was time to work the phones.

Ronald Wilson's family first. He took a deep breath and then rang the number in the file. A fragile, wavering voice answered the phone. 'Hello...'

'This is Thomas Ridpath from the Coroner's Office. I'm calling about Ronald Wilson.'

'He's not here. He passed away. They found his body at the lake. I don't know what I'm going to do.'

'Who am I speaking to?'

'Mrs Granger. Elsie Granger. I'm his grandmother.'

'I'd like to speak to his mother if I could?'

'So would I, dear. Haven't seen her for over twenty years. She left when Ronald was a toddler. We adopted him, myself and Fred. Didn't want him to go to no home. Well, he was one of our own wasn't he? Even if his mother wanted nowt to do with him.'

Ridpath scanned the file, none of this was written down.

'Fred passed away four years ago. Took it hard did, Ronald. He worshipped Fred, you know. They used to go hiking every weekend together.'

'Is there anybody else there with you, Mrs Granger?'

'No, just me now. Fred and Ronald have both gone. I suppose I'll join them soon.'

Ridpath checked the address. Bowler Street. 'Are you free at four o'clock this afternoon, Mrs Granger? I just need to go over some details with you.'

'I suppose so, but I always watch the news at six. Never miss the news me.'

'It won't take very long. See you this afternoon, Mrs Granger.'

He put down the phone. He should be able to meet this woman and then drive to pick up Polly and Eve to take them to the seven p.m. showing of the film in Didsbury. It would be tight but he should be able to make it.

Scratch that, he had to make it.

Next, a quick call to Tommy Harper to set up a meeting at Wingate Lake for the early afternoon.

'We could have lunch and then take a gander at the scene. The Fir Tree is a lovely little pub nearby, does a great home-made pizza and nifty pint of White Nancy from the Bollington Brewery,' was Tommy's reply to his request for a meeting.

'Sorry, Tommy, I already have another appointment, but I'll see you at 2:30, ok?' The last thing Ridpath wanted to do was turn up at a bereaved family's home stinking of beer.

A sad 'OK' was the only response. Next, a call to the pathologist's secretary. She confirmed Dr Schofield had already performed the post-mortem. She would check with the pathologist when the body could be released and when the report would be available.

He struck another line through his list of things to do.

Finally, a call to Charlie Whitworth. 'Hello, boss...'

'Don't you bloody boss, me. What were you doing on the M60 yesterday?'

'Driving to work in Stockfield.'

'Don't piss me about. Why did you stop on the hard shoulder?'

Ridpath rolled his eyes. 'How do you know about that?'

'Never you mind. Let's just say you're not the plod's favourite detective at the moment. In fact, if I were you I would use public transport for the foreseeable future. Harry Todd's got an all points bulletin out for you. I reckon the Traffic lads are on a bonus if they give you a ticket.'

'That bad?'

'Nah, it's worse. And you still haven't answered my question?'

'What question was that boss?' said Ridpath stalling for time.

A long sigh on the other end of the phone. 'Why were you parked up on the M60 at the place where the accident happened on Wednesday night.'

'Just checking it out, Charlie. Seeing if anything had been missed.'

'Playing bloody private detective were we?'

'It's not that, Charlie…'

'Claire Trent, my boss and yours in case you'd forgotten, issued specific instructions you were not to get involved. Remember?'

'I know but look at it from my point of view, Charlie. If you had seen a man with a gun and nobody believed you, what would you do?'

'Don't do the old trick of "put yourself in my shoes", Charlie. Remember, I was using that one with villains when you were still your father's wet dream. And secondly, people don't not believe you, we just cannot find any corroborating evidence. Your man with a gun doesn't exist, according to CCTV and the other eye witnesses.'

'Have you found the missing driver yet?'

'Nah, he's vanished, along with the car. We put out a press release through the *Evening News* but if you were driving a car with false plates would you come forward?'

'I suppose not, particularly if I was doing something bent.' Ridpath paused for a moment before asking the next question. 'And do we know who the vic is?'

'I can't tell you, Ridpath.'

'Come on, Charlie, we go back a long way. Put yourself in my shoes.'

There was a long silence on the other end of the phone. 'The fingerprint boys told me they will come back with the results this evening at five p.m.. With a bit of luck we'll know then. Toxicology should have reported too.'

'Thanks, Charlie. I won't forget this.'

'You owe me a pint. And Ridpath...'

'Yes, boss.'

'Keep your nose clean. They are still looking to pin the tail on the donkey for Wednesday. At the moment, you're it.'

'Hee haw...'

## Chapter Twenty-Three

'What have I done? Why me?'

There was a whine in Phil Marsland's voice that annoyed her.

'Why are you doing this? I've done nothing to you.'

He was stretched out on the floor, naked except for a pair of blue boxer shorts she had given him to wear.

Carrying him down from the bedroom to the cellar had been a pain. Even with her brother's strength, it was difficult manoeuvring him through the narrow doorways in the house.

At one point, he had caught his forehead on the entrance to the cellar. 'Careful, you'll hurt him,' she shouted.

'I thought that was the whole point,' he answered over his shoulder, banging Phil Marsland's head once more as they descended the stairs.

'But not yet. When he wakes up, that's when we'll do him.'

He was awake now and whining like a beaten dog. At least the smug arrogance had gone. It had taken all her composure not to wipe that stupid self-satisfied grin off his face when they had been in the pub together. She had wanted to pick up her glass and stab it into his face, watching as the sharp edges cut deep into his nose and cheeks.

But she didn't. Like the good little girl she was she kept smiling, occasionally stroking his ego and encouraging his vanity.

'You want to know why you're here, Phil?'

'Please. Please tell me. I can put it right. Whatever it is, I can make it right. My father, he…'

'We know who your father is, Phil.'

'So why are you doing this. If he finds out...'

'He'll probably kill us like he's killed lots of other people. Chopping them up and throwing them in the Mersey, isn't that his style? The body parts floating down the river to the sea.'

Phil Marsland stayed silent, his head down and his shoulders heaving as he gasped for breath.

Her brother was smoking a cigarette. She watched as the end glowed bright red with every inhalation. 'You asked us why we are doing this?'

Phil Marsland nodded his head. A few drops of sweat, and blood from his nose, dripped onto the floor.

'The simple answer is because we can, Phil.'

Her brother laughed then taking the cigarette out of his mouth, touched the hot end to Phil Marsland's shoulder.

The young man sat up screaming, 'No more, no more!'

'It's just a cigarette, Phil. And besides we haven't really started. My brother here was in Afghanistan. He learnt lots of tricks out there.'

'We had to make them talk, you see. Tell us what they knew. And sometimes they didn't want to talk. The Americans were far worse than us, far more violent. But we were far more creative. They talked to us. In the end, they always talked.'

'What do you want to know? I'll tell you everything, anything. What do you want to know?'

She bent forward and whispered in his ear. 'Let's start with your family, Phil. What was it like growing up with your father?'

# Chapter Twenty-Four

As Ridpath stopped his car at the barrier to the hospital's multi-storey car park, the familiar palpitations began. His hand began shaking as he took the parking card and drove in, finding a vacant spot on the ground floor pretty easily.

He switched off the engine and sat in the car for a moment.

He held out his hand in front of him. It was shaking as he held it over the wheel. Not even listening to John Martin's *Solid Air* during the drive from Stockfield had calmed him.

Why did he get like this? All he was doing was going for his regular check-up and a visit to the vampire to give more blood.

'Get yourself together, Ridpath,' he said out loud, 'not even Tiny McGough had this effect on you.' Tiny McGough was a 6 foot 6 inch tall bouncer who the young Constable Ridpath once had the unfortunate task of arresting after the man had done far too much speed one night. Two blows to the head with his truncheon had made Tiny blink but had little other effect. It took a sharp kick to the man's knee cap with his steel tipped boots to finally bring him down.

To this day Ridpath could still hear the crack as his boot met the knee cap. Tiny was on crutches for six weeks afterwards. He was not a happy bunny.

Ridpath had shown no fear that day, yet here he was trembling at the thought of chatting to a doctor and giving a few vials of blood.

'Sod this for a game of soldiers,' he said out loud again, switching on the engine. He would go back to Stockfield. There was a mountain of work to get done, all of it having piled up over the last two weeks, plus he had to re-read the police report on the death of Ronald Wilson before he met Tommy Harper.

He put the car in gear and stopped. How could he let Polly down? He had promised he would attend all of his outpatient clinics without fail. And what about Eve, what would she think of a dad who couldn't even face a five minute meeting with a doctor?

He turned off the engine and stepped out of the car. 'Time to face the music, Ridpath.' Of course, the music he didn't want to face was the doctor's voice. And worse, the words of 'I'm sorry to have to tell you, Mr Ridpath, but the cancer has returned.'

Hateful, horrible words, spoken in a calm, reassuring voice.

Logic told him he shouldn't have to worry. He felt okay, a little tired but not the overwhelming fatigue he had before he was diagnosed. Today would be okay. He would walk in. The doctor would tell him everything was fine. The cancer was still in remission.

Well, that was the hope anyway.

He locked the car and walked through the hospital to his clinic. It was as bustling as ever with doctors, nurses, support staff, visitors and the occasional patient in pyjamas pushing a stand with a drip.

He checked his watch. Five minutes early.

On his right the small garden looked tired and pale, a few green shoots beginning to emerge on the bushes. He had spent hours there after his time in isolation.

Anything to taste the fresh air of the day rather than the manufactured air of the isolation room. Anything to feel the warmth of the sun on his skin. Anything to hear the gentle rustle of the wind through the leaves.

He thought about going there again for a few moments to calm his nerves, but checking his watch there seemed little point. All he was doing was postponing the inevitable.

He entered the clinic and registered with the nurse behind reception. He hadn't seen her before and from her name he thought she was Spanish. When she spoke, he knew it was her nationality.

'Dyu please give blood with Nurse O'Brien, den wait for doctor to call, yes?'

She was calm and utterly charming. He sat down in one of those ugly, uncomfortable chairs hospitals seem to enjoy procuring in order to torture their patients. Looking around, there were only two other people in the room, neither of whom he recognised.

They were obviously man and wife. It looked like his second visit, because he had the look of sheer terror on his face.

Ridpath knew it well. On the first visit, he would have been told of the possibility of cancer. On this, his second visit, he would find out the reality. The tests had been done and the truth was out there, ready to kick him in the teeth and change his life forever.

Ridpath stared at him. The man knew what the doctor was going to tell him already, he just hadn't heard the words. The wife was prattling away, trying to make small talk, anything to take her mind off where she was and the words she dreaded to hear.

The man wasn't listening to her. He was in his own little world, somewhere in the future.

Ridpath had shared his ward before the chemo sent him to isolation with three other men, all older than him. He didn't bother getting to know any of them, and they didn't get to know him.

It was a cancer ward after all. There was little point in making a new friend if they were going to die. Even today the words 'cancer' and 'ward' scared the hell out of him. It was funny how two small words could produce an effect far worse than Tiny McGough.

A nurse appeared in front of him.

The vampire.

'Good morning, Mr Ridpath. Nice to see you again. Let's take a little blood, shall we.'

In his head he was screaming, 'We are not taking blood, you are, and it's not a little, but whole vials of the bloody stuff'. But he said nothing, simply grunting and standing up to follow her into a small room next to the doctor's.

'Please sit down on the edge of the couch and roll up your sleeve.' She said the last words without looking at him as she prepared the vials and syringes.

He took off his jacket and did as she asked.

'We'll take your blood pressure first.' She slipped the cuff over his arm and pumped it up, checking the results and noting them down. 'A little high today.'

It's always high when I go to hospital, he thought, what do you expect?

'Just an armful of blood.'

She made the same joke every time. She must say it a hundred times a day to a hundred different patients. He bet nobody ever laughed.

She tied off his upper arm and flicked the inside of his elbow, trying to find his vein.

'You're the one with the deep veins, aren't you?'

He didn't say anything as she pushed the syringe into his arm and screwed the vial into the back. Instantly it began to fill with rich, dark red blood.'

'Flowing like a river today.'

She unscrewed the vial and added a new one, which began to fill again.

'The doctor has asked for three vials today. That's two armfuls in layman's terms.'

Ridpath mouthed the words as she said them. It was the same old patter.

When she had finished she pressed a cotton swab into the crook of his elbow and asked him to hold it. 'There you go, easy wasn't it? Dracula has had his feast.'

That was why he called her the vampire. She called herself Dracula.

'Now let's take your weight before the doctor sees you.'

He stepped on the weighing machine and she recorded the result.

'Please go and sit down in the waiting room. The doctor will see you shortly.'

Ridpath went back and sat down, holding his arm across his chest like it was broken. In a few seconds the door to the doctor's room opened and the couple stepped out. The wife's eyes were red and the man had the wild look of shell shock. A gaze that looked at the world but saw nothing.

He heard the doctor's words. 'Please don't forget to make an appointment to come in on Friday. I'll arrange the bed for you.'

Ridpath knew the scenario well. More tests. More waiting for results. More pain and worry. All to confirm the diagnosis they had just been given.

Three terrible words. 'You have cancer'.

The cruellest words.

The man and his wife shuffled over to the receptionist. She leant around them and called his name. 'Mr Ridpath, the doctor will see you now.'

He stood up, knees trembling and strode into the doctor's room trying to think positive thoughts.

It's all going to be good.

It's just a check-up.

You feel fine.

The cancer is in remission.

He sat down facing the doctor. Dr Morris was a calm, slight, overweight man who smelt of mouthwash. He checked his notes, pushing his glasses up to the bridge of his nose.

'Good morning, Mr Ridpath, how are we feeling?'

'Great, doctor.' Ridpath lied. He was feeling okay that was all. He never felt well in hospitals. It went with the territory.

'No tiredness or lassitude?'

'Not at all, full of energy at the moment.' Ridpath lied again. The doctor sniffed, obviously not believing him.

'I see you have returned to work. How are you handling it?'

'Well. I've been given a less stressful job as a coroner's officer.' Again Ridpath lied. The job was supposed to be less stressful but that's not how it was turning out.

'Eating well, are we?'

Ridpath patted his stomach. 'Watching my diet, plenty of vegetables and fibre as you suggested.' Another lie. The last vegetable Ridpath had seen was a tomato with the fry up he had eaten on the last day of the course.

The doctor harrumphed.

'Was that good or bad?'

'Looking at your figures, you have elevated blood pressure. Nothing to worry about too much but if it continues on your next visit, we'll have to check it out. Plus, you've lost weight since your last visit.'

'I don't think so, maybe your scales are wrong.'

'No, Nurse O'Brien checked twice. You're two kilos less than a month ago.' The doctor looked at him over the top of his glasses. 'You need to take care of yourself, Mr Ridpath. It's only six months since you completed chemotherapy, your body is rebuilding its strength. Are you still smoking?'

Ridpath shook his head, but said nothing.

'I'll take that as a yes.'

'I've cut down and I haven't smoked for the last two days.'

'I don't want to sound like a broken record but you are aware of the deleterious effects of smoking on your health. I strongly recommend you cease immediately.' He glanced at his computer screen. 'How's your wife bearing up?'

'Polly? She's fine. Happy I'm back at work.'

'We often find it is the partners of those who have recovered from cancer who suffer the most. The stress of the illness affects them as much as it affects the patient.' He moved his mouse on the screen and typed in a few sentences. 'We'll check your blood work and I'll give you a call when the results are in.'

Ridpath stood up. 'Thank you, Dr Morris.'

'Mr Ridpath, I know you are a policeman, but you must give your body time to recover properly.'

'I know, doctor.'

'Knowing and doing are two different things, though, as you are well aware. I will see you next month. In the meantime, look after yourself and if you feel a cold or flu coming on, contact us immediately.'

'Yes, doctor.'

Ridpath left the doctor's room, closing the door behind him. The couple were no longer in the waiting area. No doubt they had gone somewhere to discuss the details of the diagnosis.

A discussion of the future when the future wasn't known.

As he left the waiting room, he heard the nurse call to another patient. 'Mr Dowling, the doctor will see you now.'

The words sent a shiver down Ridpath's spine.

# Chapter Twenty-Five

Tommy Harper was already waiting as Ridpath parked his car on Shillingford Road. He was a portly man; his cheeks round, flecked with red veins and a stomach dangling over his belt like yesterday's washing. An air of stale beer draped over him like a shroud. Obviously, Tommy had decided to enjoy a liquid lunch at the Fir Tree, another step in his crusade to try every beer known to man.

Ridpath remembered them both as cadets; bright-eyed and bushy-tailed before the pressures of the job had kicked in. Back in the day Tommy used to beat Ridpath in the long cross-country runs beloved of the PT instructor at Sedgley Park. Not any more though, these days he looked like he couldn't run a warm bath.

'Hiya, Ridpath, long time no see.'

'Tommy, when was the last time we met?' he said, shaking hands.

'Mike Johnson's wedding, wasn't it? Five years ago.'

'Which wife was that?'

'Number three, I think. Anyway, he's on number four now. Went to another reception about six months ago. You weren't there.'

Ridpath wondered how much Tommy knew. 'Nah, I was on leave.'

'Sick leave I heard.'

So he knew everything. 'Had a bit of a struggle with cancer. Over now, in remission.'

'Glad to hear it, mate. You're looking well.' He grabbed hold of the roll of fat hanging over his belt. 'Better than me.'

'It's the beer, Tommy.'

'Nah, mate, it's all this bloody salad the missus keeps making me eat. Bloody rabbit food.'

They were walking down Fallowfield Loop towards the lake.

'Bit out of the way, this Wingate Lake?' said Ridpath.

'That's how it got its other name.'

Ridpath turned his head towards Tommy and raised his eyebrows.

'The Secret Lake, that's what everybody says round here. Nobody calls it Wingate Lake. Don't even know where that name comes from. It's an old fishing pond that fell out of use in the Eighties. Now a few of the locals use it to walk their dogs. The local school kids skive off from school here.'

Ridpath stepped over a lump of black bin bag. 'And some people just do a bit of fly-tipping?'

'Aye, there's a lot of that going on.'

They walked up a slight path and the lake suddenly appeared before them, the water glistening in the spring sun, reeds swaying in the breeze and a few dogs barking as they ran after a ball.

'Well, I wouldn't have expected that.'

'Not many people do.' He pointed straight ahead. 'Over there is a recycling plant and to the left a cement factory. It was a rubbish dump till a few years ago but now they've started building the new estates on either side. Hate them myself. Like little boxes, no character and not a pub in sight.'

'Yet here is completely hidden.'

'Secret, ain't it?'

'Show me where the body was found?'

'Over there at the far end of the lake.'

They walked down a path, avoiding the rubbish strewn on either side.

'You working for the coroner now? Cushy number?'

Ridpath shook his head. 'Not with Margaret Challinor it's not.'

'I heard she was a bit of ball breaker.'

'No, she's good at her job. Doesn't suffer fools gladly.'

'No wonder her and Jim Howells didn't get on. He was a useless prick at anything he ever did.'

They reached the corner of the lake. It stretched in front of them like a wide river, long and thin. On their right the buzz of vehicles and crushers from the recycling plant provided a continuous drone to counterpoint the songs of the blackbirds and the robins in the trees.

'Where did you find the body?'

'Over there, in the reeds about half way up.' Tommy Harper pointed to a spot opposite a bench. 'A couple of kids from the local school were throwing a stick into the water for their dog and they saw him. Not a pretty sight.'

'Apparently he'd been in the water for two weeks.'

'That was the guess, since he was reported missing by his grandmother on April 1st.'

'I thought the pathologist had made the estimate?'

Tommy shook his head. 'Nah, he wouldn't tell me anything. It was the new chap. The young-looking one, can't remember his name.'

'Schofield.'

'That's it. Wouldn't make any commitment as to time of death. It was my guesstimate. The body was pretty decomposed plus you could see where the resident pike had taken chunks out of it.'

'Nice.'

'The kids who found it were pretty upset.'

'The post-mortem has already been performed. You should get the report for your case file in a couple of days.'

'Great, then I can close it. You know the management likes a closed case. Better for the stats.'

'Why suicide?'

'I'm sorry, what do you mean?'

'Your report was inconclusive but you didn't rule out suicide. Why?'

'I didn't see any marks of violence on the body, other than the bloody fish. And somebody called it in.'

'What?'

'We put a sign up on April 8th. You know "Have you seen this missing person". For once it worked. A woman called it in. Said she'd seen a man taking off his clothes and going into the water two weeks ago. We checked it out but didn't find anything. Three days later, the kids found the body.'

'What was the name of the woman.'

'That was the strange thing, she didn't leave her name.'

'And the kids, what did they say?'

'So many bloody questions, Ridpath, am I being interviewed?'

'Sorry, Tommy, you know what it's like. I'm new on the job and the coroner is a stickler for details. Likes everything tied up neatly.'

'Yeah, good luck with working out if this was an accident or suicide. He could have had a few drinks and gone for a swim or he could have walked into the water with the intention to drown himself. I honestly don't know which.'

'But no note and no clothes?'

'Listen, you leave a penny on the floor here and somebody will nick it. Leave clothes with a wallet on top and they won't last twenty seconds.'

'A wallet?'

Tommy sighed. 'The woman said he put his wallet on top of his clothes before he jumped in the water.'

'Do many people swim here?'

Tommy Harper laughed. 'Not the sane ones.'

None of this was in the police report. Ridpath looked around him. A couple were holding hands, their dog trying to make them throw his ball. A young woman was sitting on the park bench eating a bag of crisps as her child dozed in the pushchair. Four teenagers, still in their school uniforms, were playing football using their expensive jackets as goal posts. It was pretty busy for a Friday afternoon. 'Nobody else saw the man jumping in the lake?'

Tommy shook his head.

'Don't you think it's strange?'

'Folk keep themselves to themselves round here.'

'One last question, Tommy. Who identified the body?'

'His grandmother. Strange woman. Didn't shed a tear, just said "That's him" as if she were pointing to a bit of steak in the butchers.'

'Death hits people in different ways. We know that, Tommy.'

The other detective nodded. Then he began to kick the dirt at his feet. 'Ridpath, can you do me a favour? Can you have a chat with Charlie Whitworth, see if he has a place on MIT?'

'I'm hardly flavour of the month at the moment.'

Ridpath stared across at the water of the lake, rippling softly in the spring sunshine. A gust of wind swayed the willow trees on the banks, each branch festooned with tiny green buds reaching up to bathe in the sun.

'I got caught up in the reorganisation in 2013…'

'When they broke up CID?'

'Sent me out to J Division, didn't they? "Policing in the bloody community".' Tommy held his fingers up forming quotation marks. 'Then the boss sent me here. My detective work is chasing a few kids who've stolen bicycles, or stuff like this; blokes who top themselves after getting out of prison.'

'Ronald Wilson was an ex-con?'

'Got out four months ago. Probably couldn't handle life on the outside. Anyway, I can't hack it any more, I'm dying here.'

Ridpath scratched his head. 'You're not the only one.'

## Chapter Twenty-Six

The house was in the middle of a row of terraces on Bowler Street, not far from Reddish. Ridpath knocked on the door and stepped back.

No answer.

He checked his watch. Four p.m. Right on time. He glanced up and down the street. All the other houses were painted in a variety of colours; reds, mauves, eau-de-nil green, a light primrose yellow. All except this one. It stood out defiantly in dirty grey with paint peeling off the wood. Even the door looked like it hadn't been changed since the place was built before World War One, still with a stylised ship in stained glass in the centre of the front panel.

He knocked again.

This time there was a faint voice from inside. 'Coming.'

A minute later the door opened to reveal a short, unkempt woman wearing a pink twin piece decorated with pearls. Ridpath held out his warrant card. 'DI Ridpath from the Coroner's Office. Sorry if I woke you up. Are you Mrs Granger?'

'I was the last time I looked. And I don't do much of that any more.'

Ridpath frowned. 'Much of what?'

'Sleeping. If it's about Ronald, you'd better come in.'

He followed her down the hall, past a picture of Jesus with a red light where his heart should be, and a small bowl of holy water. They turned into a small room on the right. She walked unsteadily, a Zimmer frame supporting her every step. The place had that old people's smell; a tired mustiness combined with a tinge of pee and the aroma of age.

She inched across the tiny room. The heat was sweltering; a gas fire glowing brightly and the windows tightly closed. Near to the fire an old armchair was surrounded by balls of wool, pattern sheets and discarded knitting. Above it a large ornamental clock ticked loudly, the second hand jerking each time it moved forward. In the corner the television was on with the sound turned down but the subtitles on.

She saw him looking at the television. 'I've gone a bit deaf in my old age, but my eyes are still as sharp as knitting needles.' Ridpath was not sure that was true but said nothing.

The woman dropped heavily into the arm chair. 'The knees are gone too. Too much scrubbing steps and floors when I were young. Were you the one who rang me this morning?'

Ridpath took a seat opposite, opening his notebook. 'That was me, Mrs Granger. I've come about your grandson, Ronald...'

'He's not here.'

For a moment Ridpath worried if the old woman was suffering from senility. He decided to start again. 'Mrs Granger, I'm from the Coroner's Office...'

'You've already said that. If you're here to tell me he's dead, I already know. I saw him lying in a white room with a sheet over him. Took care of him since he was a baby. Well, me and Fred. Towered over both of us he did. He were always a big lad even when he was in school. Bit of a tearaway. I had the police around here a few times, I tell you. But he weren't a bad lad, just boisterous.'

'He lived with you?'

'Well he couldn't live with his mother, she ran off down south with a new fella not long after Ronald were born. Myself and his granddad brought him up. Then, after Fred died, I looked after him. Or, I should say, he looked after me.'

'Exactly how old was Ronald when he died?'

Only the sound of the clock broke through the silence as Mrs Granger counted on her fingers. 'He were born in February 1995, so that would make him twenty-three. They said he drowned, but I don't believe them.'

'Why?'

'Ronald couldn't swim. Never learned, was afraid of the water. So why would he go swimming in the Secret Lake?'

Ridpath didn't tell her that if he wanted to commit suicide not being able to swim was an advantage. 'A witness saw him take off his clothes and jump into the water.'

The old woman turned and stared at Ridpath. 'I don't believe it. Ronald would never take off his clothes in public. He were shy. Oh sorry love, where's my manners? Would you like a cuppa?' She tried to lever herself off the arm chair, but fell back.

'You want me to make it?'

'Would you love? These knees of mine are giving me gyp today.'

He walked through to the kitchen. It was spotless in a totally unused way. He filled the kettle full of water and placed it on the gas ring.

'I don't use the pot any more, but you'll find a couple of mugs draining beside the sink and the teabags are on the counter.'

Ridpath put the mugs down and added the teabags, one for each cup. He went to the fridge for milk but it was empty. A half used loaf, a tub of spreadable margarine, two eggs and a shrivelled tomato. No milk.

He went back to the lounge. 'You don't have any milk?'

'The neighbour's not done my shopping this week. She's the same neighbour who rang the police for me when he went missing. A big fat policeman came round. Not a bit as handsome as you.' She paused for a moment as Ridpath blushed. 'Ronald always did it every Friday morning when he were here. We sometimes went together if he wasn't busy. I love going round supermarkets. So much more to see than when I was a girl. It's so dear though, I'm surprised the young ones can afford to eat. You'll find milk powder in the cupboard.'

Ridpath went back and found it sitting next to two cans of beans and a packet of dried soup.

He made the tea and took it through to Mrs Granger.

'I do love a cup of tea,' she said holding the cup with both hands and taking a large gulp.

'Where did Ronald work, Mrs Granger?'

'He didn't. Well, not much anyway since he got out of prison. Never could hold down a job. People didn't like Ronald. But he was good boy.'

'Prison?'

'When he were nineteen. They said he assaulted a policeman. But I know Ronald, he wouldn't have done anything like that.'

'When did he get out?'

'Four months ago. I remember because it were just before Christmas.'

Ridpath wondered whether this was an accident or a classic case of suicide like Tommy Harper had said; a former prisoner who just couldn't handle the world outside. 'Did he have any close friends?'

She thought for a moment. 'Not really. Before he went to prison, he was out with the lads every night. Since his release, he tried to stay away, kept himself to himself.'

'Did he see his probation officer?'

'Once, I think. After that, he was contacted by phone. He said the man was a waste of time.'

From Ridpath's experience of the new probation service, Ronald Wilson wasn't wrong.

Mrs Granger suddenly sat upright, almost spilling her tea. 'But he had a new girlfriend. He told me. Lovely girl she was too, he said.'

'What was her name?'

'I don't know. Never met her even though I asked. He said he would introduce us when she was ready.'

Ridpath closed his notebook. The tea lay next to his foot untouched. 'I have to tell you Mrs Granger, the pathologist has completed his post-mortem examination of Ronald's body.'

'They cut him up?'

'I'm afraid it's routine in cases such as this to perform a post-mortem. I should be able to tell you soon when your undertaker can collect the body for burial or cremation.'

'But I don't have an undertaker.'

'Do you have anybody, a relative or a neighbour, who could help you arrange the funeral?'

She shook her head. 'There was a woman who came three times a week from the council when Ronald was inside. She was lovely and we had such good chats. But she stopped coming a while ago. Told me there wasn't any money any more. The old priest, Father Donovan, used to come here, but he died and there's a new young fella I don't like. Wears a leather jacket. Now, have you ever heard of a priest in a leather jacket? Since he came to the parish, I don't even go to mass any more. But I still says my prayers every night in case He's listening.'

Ridpath thought for a moment. 'OK, leave it to me. I'll arrange for somebody to help you.' Ridpath didn't know how yet, but he would make it happen. Pensioners like Mrs Granger shouldn't be left on their own.

He checked the ancient clock on the mantelpiece loudly ticking away time. 'I have to go now, Mrs Granger, but I'll come back tomorrow to let you know what's happening.'

The old woman tried to get up.

'Please stay where you are, I'll see myself out.'

'Now, make sure you bless yourself with the holy water on the way out. We wouldn't want anything to be happening to you.'

'I will,' answered Ridpath, already deciding that he wouldn't.

He walked to the door, turning back to take last look at the old woman. She was staring into the air, her filmy eyes looking at nothing in particular, her wrinkled fingers lying motionless on her lap.

Above her head, the clock, and its jerky second hand, ticked on.

## Chapter Twenty-Seven

Ridpath sat in the car outside Mrs Granger's house and made a call to social services to see what they could do regarding the funeral of Ronald Wilson. He listened to a polite but firm recorded message, stating the opening hours and giving another number in case of an emergency.

Was this an emergency? Probably not, it would wait till Monday. The pathologist still hadn't officially released the body anyway. More of a worry was Mrs Granger. Would she be able to manage on her own?

He glanced at the dashboard clock, Eve and Polly would be waiting for him but there was just enough time to make another phone call.

He pressed speed dial on his mobile.

'This is not a good time, Ridpath.' Charlie Whitworth sounded grumpier than usual.

'I was just ringing to see if the toxicology and the fingerprints results had come in for our M60 vic.'

'They have.'

'And?'

There was a moment's silence before Charlie let out a long sigh. 'Toxicology says there were no significant quantities of drugs in his system at the time of his death. There were slight traces of cocaine and marijuana, but the lab thinks they were probably from use at least a week ago. There was a stronger trace of a sleeping pill, Ambien, though. Perhaps our vic had insomnia.'

'So he was clean, Charlie?'

'As clean as any person walking the streets of Manchester. But that's not all.'

'The fingerprints?'

'The ones from the bonnet of your car came back with a clear match.'

'To?'

'A certain Gerard Connelly.'

'Shit.'

'Shit is the word, Ridpath.'

'Not one of *the* Connellys?'

'The youngest son of Michael Connelly.'

'Shit.'

'I'm just about to go over to Eccles to tell him. Claire Trent has just put us on full alert and all leave has been cancelled. We've taken the truck driver into protective custody and we're battening down the hatches in case a gang war erupts on the streets of Manchester.'

'Is Michael still running the Eccles mob?'

'Him and his other son, Graham. The son's out of prison at the moment.'

'When did that happen?'

'Late last year, for good bloody behaviour.'

'Jesus, the Connellys wouldn't know good behaviour if it kicked them up the arse.'

Charlie Whitworth chuckled. 'Claire Trent is spitting brass tacks. Her carefully constructed story about a crazy druggie who brought the M60 to a halt has fallen apart.'

'Does that mean you're starting to believe me about the man with a gun?'

'Let's just say it might have a wee bit more credence than thirty minutes ago.'

'You need to look at the area around Sale Water Park. Somebody chased our vic through there before he tried to cross the M60.'

'Listen, Ridpath, it might be a good time to show your face round the office. MIT is really stretched right now. She's even called in help from the serious crime boys. It's every hand on deck.'

'She must be desperate.' Ridpath was about to say he would be right over when he remembered Polly and Eve waiting for him at his mother-in-law's house. Perhaps he could take them another time.

'I'll be right over… tomorrow morning, boss. I need to be with Polly and Eve this evening. They are waiting for me.'

Ridpath heard the brakes of a car scream to a stop at the junction in front of him. For a moment he thought it was Charlie Whitworth's voice. Instead he heard an answer in calm, measured terms.

'Don't say you weren't given a chance, Ridpath.'

Ridpath would have preferred the scream.

The phone clicked off. He sat there for a moment staring at the black mobile in his hand. Perhaps, he should go to MIT. This could be his chance to get back on the team, show both Trent and Charlie Whitworth he was still a good copper despite the bloody cancer.

He put the car in gear and pulled away from the kerb.

'Sod them.' He was a good copper but his wife and child meant more to him than any bloody job. He was going to spend a night with Polly and Eve and watch *Coco the Clown* or whatever the movie was.

Tomorrow was another day.

But tonight was for his family.

# Chapter Twenty-Eight

'Right, Dave. You're driving me.'

'Where are we going, boss?'

Dave Hardy picked up his coat from the hanger as Charlie walked out of the door.

'We're off to see Michael Connelly.'

'That toe-rag? What's he done now?'

'It's not what he's done, Dave, it's what's been done to him.'

The lift doors opened. A uniform from the sixth floor, his shoulders covered in silver braid, was already there.

'Evening, sir.'

'Evening, Charlie.'

They both bustled into the lift.

'Going home, sir?'

'Not this early, Charlie. Drinks with the Manchester Business Entrepreneurs Association.'

Charlie turned his back to face the door. 'Sounds fun, sir,' he said over his shoulder.

'A barrel of laughs. How's the M60 case coming along?'

'New developments, sir.'

'Oh? And what are…'

The lift doors opened and Charlie raced out without answering, followed by Dave Hardy, leaving the assistant chief constable on his own.

'Tosser.' Charlie said out loud when they were far enough away.

Dave Hardy was almost running to keep up with him. 'Should have answered him, Charlie. It doesn't help to piss them off.'

'Let Claire Bloody Trent handle the wankers, that's what she gets paid for.'

Dave Hardy opened the door of their car. A beat-up silver Vauxhall Vectra that had seen more detectives in it than a Manchester hooker.

'Couldn't you get anything better from the pool, Dave?'

'It's all they had, boss. The cutbacks…'

'Is that the answer to everything these days?'

'Yeah,' was Dave's monosyllabic reply.

He started the engine. It coughed a few times before finally firing. Putting it in gear, he drove through the raised barrier and out of the HQ car park, turning right on Oldham Road.

'You still haven't answered my question, boss.'

'Forty-two.'

'What?'

'The answer to the meaning of life.'

'No, I asked what Michael Connelly had done. Last time, it was armed robbery. He got off with that. But we haven't been to his place for a while. He's been quiet.'

'He's not been quiet, just more careful. We're still looking into him for those hammer murders in 2005. And I'm pretty sure he was the one who shot Reuben Chalmers in Cheetham Hill.'

'There was no evidence, boss.'

'There never bloody is. But one day we'll find it.'

'So why are we going there?'

'His son's been found dead on the M60.'

'Ridpath's case?'

'The one and only.'

Dave Hardy let out a long whistle. 'Fuck me sideways.'

'You and half the rest of GMP.'

'What are we going to do?'

'Do? We're going to tell him.'

Dave looked away from the road. 'Shouldn't we have brought a few more men. He's not going to be pleased.'

'Keep your eyes on the road, Dave, didn't they teach you at police driving school?'

The detective switched back to stare out through the windscreen.

'Nah, it'll just be us two, Dave, keep it low-key.'

There was silence in the car for a few minutes. Finally, Dave Hardy leant forward to switch on the radio.

His hand was covered by Charlie's giant mitt. 'Not now, Dave. I need to think. It's not often you have the pleasure of telling a man his son is dead. And even rarer when that man is a thug like Michael Connelly. I have to work out the correct form of words.'

'I always hated giving bad news, me. I remember once having to tell a con's mother that her son had been stabbed in prison. Went through all the guff they teach you. "Sorry to have to tell you. Our deepest commiserations". All the usual rigmarole. She of course, broke down in tears, scriking like a banshee. I got a phone call five minutes later. I'd told the wrong mother. Her son was the one who did the stabbing. He ended up serving another fifteen years inside.'

'You tell the nicest stories, Dave.'

Rain began to splatter on the windshield. A typical spring day in Manchester. Sunshine followed by showers. All they needed now was hailstones.

'So have you worked out what to tell Michael Connelly to cause him the least pain?'

Charlie shook his head. 'Nah, but I've worked out how to tell him to cause him the most.'

Inside he was pleased he was the bearer of ill tidings. There were some perks to being a copper. And this was definitely one of them.

# Day Four

*Saturday, April 21, 2018*

## Chapter Twenty-Nine

The meeting was just about to begin when Ridpath arrived. Charlie Whitworth was standing at the door. 'So you got my message?'

The WhatsApp had arrived that morning.

*Be at MIT. 8:30. That's an order not a request.*

'It was as succinct as ever Charlie.'

'You know me, Ridpath, I hate to waste words when they are not needed. How's Polly?'

'Good.'

In truth, last night was better than good. Coco was a strange subject for a kid's cartoon: the Mexican Day of the Dead. But it was all handled with such verve and style it could be enjoyed by both kids and adults. The story resonated with Ridpath as he understood his own brush with mortality last year. Eve enjoyed it for the music and the action, and the young kid following his dream. But Polly was more affected. Almost as the story of bringing up a family alone after the death of a husband touched her deeply.

Afterwards they had eaten ice cream together and enjoyed being a family once more. He had told them of Mrs Granger and her sad, lonely existence.

'Why don't you go and see her, Daddy?' said Eve. 'We do it at school, visiting the old people's home to say hello and sing songs. They're so nice. I always feel good after I've been.'

'Why don't you pop round with some food to tide her over the weekend, then you can contact social services on Monday.

I'll check if there are any church groups in the area who work with old people,' suggested Polly. 'With all the cuts, the police and teachers are bloody social workers these days. You may as well do your job.'

So that morning he had risen early, driving round to the local 24-hour Tesco to get some milk, bread, tea bags, butter, eggs, bacon, cabbage and potatoes. All the basics, adding three ready-made Irish stews and a couple of salmon dinners she could microwave if she didn't feel like cooking. He had driven round to her place and knocked on the door. She had answered it almost immediately this time.

'Who are you?'

'DI Ridpath We met yesterday, remember?'

A flash of recognition in the rheumy eyes. 'You asked me about Ronald. I need to bury him.'

'Right, but we'll sort it out next week. Here's some groceries for the weekend. The neighbour asked me to give them you.' She wouldn't refuse if they were from the neighbour.

'She remembered. I was a bit worried as I'm not as steady as I used to be. Can't get to the shops any more.'

He placed the food in her cupboard and fridge, showing her where he had put them and making a cup of tea before he left.

'You're not having one?'

'I have to get to work, Mrs Granger. A meeting. But I'll see you on Monday about the funeral.'

He left, closing the door firmly behind him, making a mental note to ring the local plods and ask them to keep an eye on her. For once Ridpath felt good about himself. His daughter was right, it was good to give back to others.

A murmur amongst the assembled detectives brought him back down to earth. Detective Superintendent Claire Trent danced through the crowd accompanied by a tall, austere man wearing glasses, looking like they had been stolen from the Milky Bar Kid.

The meeting room was set up for a presentation with a computer hooked up to a projector. At the moment the screen was displaying the words 'Operation Lollipop'.

'Another bloody PowerPoint presentation,' said DS Hardy as he walked in. He looked up at the screen and said, 'Lollipop? You are shitting me.'

'That's what she's decided to call it, Dave.'

'Does she know what it's slang for?'

Charlie shrugged his shoulders.

Claire Trent took her place at the front of the room and clapped her hands. 'Right, everyone.'

Ridpath took a seat between Charlie and Dave.

'I've called this urgent briefing because of events on Wednesday. If you remember our own DI Ridpath,' she nodded in his direction, 'called in an accident on Wednesday evening. The victim in the accident has been identified as Gerard Connelly.'

A buzz went round the room.

'It seems most of you have heard about him. He's the son of the leader of the Eccles gang, Michael Connelly. At the moment, the jury is out whether this really was an accident or the beginning of a gangland war. If it's the latter we are going to be ready and prepared to take action at any time of the day or night. I have already cancelled all leave for MIT for the foreseeable future. I've asked Detective Chief Inspector Robinson from the North West Serious and Organised Crime Squad to brief us this morning.'

'Good man, Robbo,' said Charlie under his breath.

'One of DCI Robinson's teams will be based in MIT for the duration.'

Dave Hardy put up his hand. 'I thought this accident was just another druggie taking a walk along the M60, playing chicken with the traffic.'

Claire Trent reddened slightly. 'Toxicology suggests there were only traces of drugs in his system. We—'

She was about to continue speaking when Dave Hardy asked another question. 'Does Michael Connelly know about his son yet?'

She nodded at Charlie Whitworth, who stood up to answer.

'I told him last night. He wasn't best pleased. His actual words were, "I'm going to get that effing driver if it's the last thing I do".'

'So he doesn't know I saw a gunman chasing him?' asked Ridpath.

He saw Charlie glance across at Claire Trent before he answered. 'No, I didn't tell him.'

'So you see now why all leave has been cancelled. I'd like to...'

Dave Hardy put his hand up. 'What about DI Ridpath's report of an armed man chasing the victim?'

A slow smile spread across Charlie's face. Ridpath realised they were winding her up, toying with her like a cat plays with a mouse.

'We haven't discounted this and will continue to investigate. No CCTV images have confirmed DI Ridpath's report.'

'But surely with the identity of the victim now confirmed, this could have been a gangland hit gone wrong.'

'We're still looking into it. Enough with the questions or we'll never be finished. I'm going to hand it over to DCI Robinson from the Serious and Organised Crime Squad for his briefing.'

Another glance from Dave across to Charlie Whitworth.

'Right,' he said, rubbing his hands together and pressing the key on the computer. A slide appeared bearing the logo of his department, as if the coppers in the room didn't know where he was from. 'Organised crime is on the rise. Illicit national and transnational groups have flourished in recent years, expanding across borders and continents. Russian Mafia. North Korean cyber-attacks. Eastern European slave traffickers. Albanian cocaine smugglers. Chinese drug manufacturers. Whilst in the

UK we're facing a whole host of new threats. Hundreds of billions of pounds laundered through London every year. A dramatic rise in the murder rate in the capital in four years. Historic child abuse in Rotherham. Fentanyl manufacturers in Merseyside and Manchester. Drug dealers working out of the main cities moving into the county towns. As well as a host of terrorist, IT, credit card, identity thefts and child abuse online.'

'Shit, it scares me and I'm a copper.'

'It should do, Dave. Organised crime, illicit national and transnational networks have multiplied since the 1980s and now make an annual £1.5 trillion around the world and £37 billion, or 1.8 per cent of GDP in Britain. It's a big money, national business. And, as police, we're still running forty-three separate forces, each looking after their own little patch.'

'Bobbies on the beat, mate, that's what Joe Public wants.'

'But bobbies on the beat are never going to stop these sorts of crimes.'

'But what about the gangs in Manchester, Robbo?' Claire Trent brought him back to the job at hand.

'Manchester has been relatively quiet since the late 1990s. The days of the Gooch Close Gang, Pepperhill Mob, the Doddington Gang and the Longsight Crew running wild with guns have thankfully long passed. That's not to say they still don't exist. We all know they do.' He pressed a key and a table appeared on the screen. 'Here is a stat for the number of gang-related incidents for the north-west since 2000. As you see, Liverpool has dominated the scene for a long while...'

'The Scousers finally on top of something, maybe Liverpool might manage to win the league this year,' Dave Hardy shouted out, followed by laughter from the other detectives.

DCI Robinson carried on without smiling. 'There was a spike in Manchester-related incidents with the murder of reputed gangland leader Con Morgan in Salford.'

'Aye, haven't we charged somebody for that?'

'The case is up before the courts as we speak. As you can imagine, it is sub judice at the moment.'

'Is the decline in the Manchester gang incidents because we put O'Shea away?'

'That and the death of two of the brothers; one from a heart attack and the other stabbed to death by his girlfriend. But intelligence tells us the reason for the lack of incidents is simple. The four main Manchester gangs reached an informal agreement to divide up the city into areas of influence.'

'What're their major activities?'

'The same as ever. Drugs; the ecstasy market has declined but new drugs have replaced it, crack, spice, cocaine and metamphetamine. The latest drug on the rise is fentanyl, a hundred times stronger than heroin. Manchester is supposed to be the centre for its manufacture in the UK.'

'Which gang is doing that?'

Robbo shrugged his shoulders. 'To be honest, we don't know. We haven't seen a rise in the use of opioids like America yet, but mark my words, it's only a matter of time.'

'They're still in the other rackets like robbery, prostitution, gambling, extortion and pornography?'

'Prostitution and extortion, yes. Gambling and pornography, not so much. The Internet has broken their monopoly on those vices. Whilst armed robbery, the go-to crime to fund the drug trade in the early 2000s has all but died out.'

'Why?'

'One explanation is you lot have made it far too dangerous…'

A burble of laughter spread around the room.

'…But don't congratulate yourselves too soon. A more likely reason is the drugs trade is now self-financing. They are making so much money they don't have to resort to robbing post offices to fund it any more.'

'Anything new they are moving into?'

'This may sound strange but security seems to be one of the areas they are developing and, as you see with the number of construction projects in Manchester, we believe they have moved rapidly into property development and the building trade. Taxis and transportation seem to be another area where they are expanding, particularly Michael Connelly. Any more questions?'

There was a collective shake of the head. The screen changed again.

'According to our latest intelligence, here are the four main gangs operating in the city at the moment. The Eccles mob, run by this man.' A blurred black and white picture of a rotund Michael Connelly appeared on the screen.

'Ugly bugger, ain't he?'

'Sixty-two years old, born in 1956, he's spent twenty-two of those years in jail...'

'Who says crime doesn't pay...?'

DCI Robinson ignored the interruptions.

'Married with three kids, two boys and a girl.'

'Where does he find the bloody time?'

'The eldest, Graham Connelly, is following in dad's footsteps.'

'Which one is our vic?'

'He's the second son, Gerard Connelly. A few minor convictions and served three months on remand at Risley. But, for the most part, has kept his nose clean.'

'What's the Connellys' source of income?'

'The usual; drugs, prostitution and extortion. But of late, they have been moving their money into transport and property development. As with all gangs, this is an attempt to legitimise themselves, led by Graham. This son is an interesting character. He was charged with assault on a young boy aged twelve, two years ago, but managed to get off on a technicality and a lot of Daddy's money.'

'Just what we need, another paedo on the streets,' muttered Dave Hardy under his breath.

The screen changed and the words Salford appeared in block letters. Robbo carried on speaking.

'The next gang is based in Salford. After the murder of its reputed head honcho, Con Morgan in 2013, it was taken over by his number two, Big Terry Marsland.' Another picture appeared on the screen of a tall, shaven headed man. 'Ex-nightclub bouncer and fitness fanatic, Terry is not to be trifled with. He quickly and violently imposed himself on Salford and until now, we believed he had an informal truce with Michael Connelly. He has one son and one daughter both involved up to their necks in his business. Philip and Tracy...'

'Where do they get these names?' asked Dave Hardy and was answered by laughing from the other detectives.

Robbo ignored him. 'Any other questions?'

When there weren't any, he pressed another key on his computer. Another picture appeared on the screen, this time taken in a police station during an arrest.

'The third lot in the frame for this is the Cheetham Hill mob. They're mostly into drugs with a side salad of "protection" services. They keep themselves to themselves and are led by Ahmed Yousof. They've been leading the expansion of the drug trade across the county borders particularly into the smaller towns of Cheshire and Wales.

'The final mobster in our rogues' gallery runs the Moss Side Yardies. While not as powerful as the gangs of the 1990s, they still are a strong force in the area, particularly in drugs and prostitution. This is Tony Ryder, the boss. The scar across his face came from a knife fight when he was sixteen. According to intelligence he has been building up an arsenal over the last six months.'

'Where's he getting his guns?'

'From London, a dealer called Peter Dominguez. He's been around for years but nobody has ever pinned anything on him. Most seem to be reconfigured Makarovs from the Eastern Bloc, but we've heard whispers of Uzis and Armalites being part of his latest offering.'

A collective whistle came from the gathered detectives.

'Why?' asked Ridpath.

Robinson shrugged his shoulders.

'Why what?'

'Why is Tony Ryder suddenly arming up? I thought they all had an agreement?'

'Your guess is as good as mine. He could be wanting to expand, recapture the glory days of the 1990s. Who knows with these thugs.'

Claire Trent stepped forward. 'Any more questions?'

A collective shake of the head.

'Right, gentlemen and ladies. We're going to sit on these four gangs for the next week. Charlie, I want your team in unmarked cars watching the Connellys.'

'Yes, ma'am.'

'I also want you to follow up on Gerard Connelly. His father told you they hadn't seen him for three days previous to Wednesday?'

'That's right.'

'Find out where he's been. We didn't find a mobile at the scene, but do we know his number?'

'The father refused to give it me.'

'You explained we could trace his whereabouts through the mobile masts and his calls, and he still said no?'

Charlie nodded. 'Wanted to talk to his solicitor first.'

'Bastard,' she swore. 'Well, track down his car. Perhaps we can trace his movements through ANPR and CCTV.'

'They wouldn't give me that either.'

'Well, pull your finger out and get on to DVLA in Swansea. Get Chrissy Wright to help you.'

'Yes, ma'am.'

'Lorraine...' A woman who Ridpath had never seen before stood up.

'Can you and Catherine introduce yourselves to the team?'

Another young woman with short blonde hair rose from her chair next to Lorraine.

The young woman started to speak in a clear, authoritative voice. 'My name is Catherine Delaney. I'm twenty-five years old, a detective sergeant. I was born in Manchester and work with DI Lorraine Caruso in Bolton.'

'They're getting bloody younger,' whispered Dave Hardy out of the side of his mouth.

The older woman spoke next. 'My name is Lorraine Caruso. I'm not going to tell you buggers what my age is. Married with two kids and a detective inspector attached to Bolton CID working with Catherine for the last year or so.'

A few murmured welcomes to which Lorraine nodded her head.

'Great.' Claire Trent clapped her hands once. 'I want your team watching Big Terry's mob, Lorraine.'

'No problems, guvnor.'

'Steve, I want you to take Cheetham Hill. And Robbo, your team knows the Moss Side mob so can you be on them, please?'

'Of course, Claire.'

'We're not going to have another gangland war like the days of Gunchester, not on my bloody watch. Right, get on it.' She clapped her hands to end the briefing. 'Charlie and DI Ridpath, in my room. Now.'

Ridpath glanced across at his DCI and mouthed, 'What does she want?'

Charlie Whitworth smiled enigmatically and shrugged his shoulders.

# Chapter Thirty

'Right, what are you two up to?'

The question came as soon as Ridpath closed the door. Claire Trent stood behind her desk, putting it between herself and the two detectives.

Ridpath glanced across at Charlie Whitworth. 'I don't know what you mean, ma'am.'

'You think I don't know Dave Hardy is one of your buddies. Why all the questions?'

Charlie shrugged his shoulders. 'I presume he wanted to know about the inquiry, ma'am.'

'And make me look like a bloody fool in front of Robinson and his team?'

'I think you're overreacting here, boss...'

'Am I Charlie? Am I being too feminine for you? Too girly? Well, listen to me, if I have one more scene like we just had, you'll be out on your arse, running the bloody bogs in Belle Vue nick, do I make myself clear, DCI Whitworth?'

Ridpath saw Charlie grit his jaw, the muscle flexing at the side of his face. 'Very clear, ma'am.'

'And don't think anybody can protect you. People have long memories in GMP. You and John Gorman ruffled a few feathers in your time. After the Beast of Manchester fiasco, some people feel it's time to do some plucking.'

'I resent that, ma'am. We had strong evidence of Dalbey's guilt.'

'You managed to put an innocent man away for ten years, Charlie. If it weren't for Margaret Challinor's work, he would still be in prison.'

Ridpath noticed she made no mention of his part in the affair.

'That's unfair, ma'am...'

She held up her hand to stop him talking. When she spoke again the tone had changed, becoming warmer, more empathetic. 'Look, Charlie, I think you're a good copper, but there are people in management who believe MIT needs a shake up after the John Gorman era. That's why they brought me in. I would prefer you to stay on, but if I have to put up with another showing like this morning, well...'

She left the last part of the sentence unsaid.

She glanced at her expensive watch. 'Now, I have a meeting with the chief constable to explain to him why we could be at the start of a major gang war to make the days of Gunchester look like a vicar's tea party.'

'It may not be a gang war...'

They both stared at Ridpath.

'Explain yourself,' said Claire Trent.

'Well, I only saw one man chasing Gerard Connelly.'

'The man with the gun?'

Ridpath nodded. 'If it were a gangland killing I would expect there to be more people involved, not just one shooter.'

'They could have brought a hitman in from Liverpool or Birmingham,' said Charlie.

'But why? It doesn't make sense. The gangs of Manchester have an agreement, they are raking in acres of cash, why mess it up? Even back in 2013, when Morgan was murdered, Manchester remained quiet, why start a war now?'

Claire Trent stayed silent for a moment. 'Those are good questions, Ridpath. The worse thing we can do at the moment is to jump to conclusions without any real evidence.' She looked up at Charlie fixing him with her green eyes. 'Find out what's going on. Leave no stone unturned, understand? Use any and all resources, intelligence, confidential informants. Whatever you need, you've got.'

'What about Robbo. He's probably got the best intelligence?'

'I want MIT to sort this out, not Serious and Organised Crime. We've had to call them in because the chief constable demanded it, but *we're* going to make this go away, not bloody Robbo.'

'What do you want me to do?' asked Ridpath.

'You're going to be my eyes and ears with Michael Connelly, Ridpath.'

'What? I'm supposed to be working with the coroner.'

'Exactly, in that role you have to liaise with him regarding his son. It will give you an opportunity to visit his home without him knowing you are GMP.'

'But doesn't it compromise my position with the coroner?'

She made a moue with her mouth. Ridpath noticed the red lipstick had begun to clump around on her top lip, leaving little goblets of red in the cracks in her lips.

'Last time I looked at the budgets, your salary was still being paid by my department and you were still on my books…'

'But…'

'And I've already had a chat with Margaret Challinor and she agrees you will be the best person to liaise with the Connellys regarding the funeral of their son. It is part of the duties of a coroner's officer, isn't it?'

'Yes, but…'

'So, I want to know what's happening in their family. If anybody farts and there's no smell, I want to know, understand?'

Ridpath nodded.

She stood up, pulling down her black jacket. 'Time to meet the management. You two better get going too.'

They both stood up. When Charlie reached the door she spoke again.

'Before I forget, Charlie. Get rid of Dave Hardy. Transfer him to Traffic or something. I don't want him on the team any more. Is that clear?'

Charlie Whitworth's jaw clenched and unclenched. 'Yes, ma'am,' he answered without turning back.

'And Charlie, there's an awful lot of willies waving in your department. Replace him with a woman. I want a better gender balance in MIT.'

Charlie sighed. 'Yes, ma'am.'

# Chapter Thirty-One

They both walked back to DCI Whitworth's office, neither one of them speaking or looking at the other.

Once inside Charlie threw his file onto the table. 'You should not have witnessed that Ridpath. No senior officer should ever be reprimanded in front of a junior.'

'I think she was making a point.'

'Making a point? She just drove a hole in me big enough to park a tractor.'

'What are you going to do about Dave Hardy?'

His boss looked at him with dagger eyes. 'I don't bloody know. Luckily, he had a chat with me earlier. He wants something quieter and less stressful with regular hours; his missus is complaining she never sees him.'

'I know the problem.'

Charlie Whitworth ran his fingers through his thinning hair. 'I'll find him something. He's a bloody good copper is Dave, but he's been tired for a long while. Time for him to move on.' Suddenly, the eyes glanced towards Ridpath. 'If you think you can replace him you've got another think coming. For one, he's a DS and you're already an inspector. And secondly, you have to show a bit more loyalty before I let you back on the team, Ridpath. I want people I can trust to be by my side not stab me in the back.'

'I've never stabbed you in the back, boss.'

'But you've not been by my side either, have you?'

'I thought our job was to stop the bad guys not take sides.'

Charlie shook his head. 'You always were a naive sod, Ridpath.'

'Anyway, I wasn't thinking about me. I was asking for Tommy Harper. He's dying out in Reddish.'

'Fat Tommy? He's still drinking his way through the beers of Manchester?'

Ridpath shrugged his shoulders. 'I wouldn't know. Apparently, he's the reverse of Dave Hardy. He wants to spend less time with the missus.'

'Probably the other way round if you ask me. Anyway, you heard Her Majesty, she wants a bloody woman for the team.'

'She's got a point. Since Sarah Castle died, it's become very male.'

Charlie stayed silent, staring down at the ground for a moment.

For a moment, Ridpath flashed back to the young woman detective sergeant murdered by Harold Lardner, her smile beaming at him as they negotiated the workload on the Beast of Manchester case. For some reason he had never erased the voicemail she had left him on his mobile. As if by removing her message, he would remove her memory. He had never told anybody, but sometimes she came to him in his dreams, always saying the same thing. 'Don't give up, Ridpath, never give up.'

'Sarah was a good officer, but she was a loose cannon that's why she was targeted by the Beast,' Charlie said finally.

'She was targeted because she got too close to him.'

Charlie's eyes flared with anger. 'See what I mean about loyalty, Ridpath? You can't stop rubbing my nose in it. Don't you think I know I screwed up and that's going to stay with me for the rest of my life.'

There was a long silence between the two of them before Ridpath finally said, 'There's one other problem I didn't tell Claire Trent.'

Charlie's eyebrow raised. 'Oh?'

'I was on your team when we arrested Michael Connelly six years ago.'

A small smile appeared at the edge of Charlie's lips. 'That may be a problem, Ridpath, but luckily it's yours not mine.'

# Chapter Thirty-Two

The woman and her brother sat in the white van for five minutes, checking the car park and the church for any signs of movement.

Nothing.

'Let's get going,' she ordered.

They ran to the back doors. He had found a decal online for a plumber and attached it to the side of their white van, changing the number plates too.

Of course, the van had been her idea. It was now one of those ubiquitous vehicles everybody sees but nobody notices.

She opened the back doors. Phil Marsland was lying on a plastic sheet in the rear, naked except for a pair of blue boxers.

She never knew why she always dressed their victims. At first, it had been a matter of expediency; to give them something to wear when their clothes had been soiled after their skin had been burnt with cigarettes. But now, it just looked right. There was something pleasing about the young male body in boxer shorts.

Even more pleasing when they were dead.

The car park was empty as it always was on a Saturday afternoon, their spot hidden from the main road and Barton Bridge beyond. She had her brother park with the engine facing outwards. Even on the off chance somebody came in, all they would see was a white van with its back doors open.

She glanced up at the church, its spire and dark, satanic stone looming over them. She shivered: a hateful place. That was why she had chosen it. The CCTV on the corner of the roof was staring right down at them like a watchful eye. A good job she had smashed the lens two days ago. The monument was just ten yards away.

She didn't know why she had chosen this place, it just seemed right. Open enough for the body to be discovered, not too isolated. The position, close to the junction between Eccles, Salford and Manchester, appealed to her sense of theatre. They would all know here was where the territories of the various gangs met.

'You cover the body with a sheet and carry it over to the monument. But first I have to finish the job.' She picked up a large kitchen knife and reached over to grab Phil Marsland's penis, pulling it upwards. 'He won't need this anymore.'

With one swipe of the knife the penis came away from the body. She held the small sausage like object in her hand. 'I'll keep this as a souvenir.' She stuffed it in her pocket. 'Carry him over there.'

She always admired the strength of her brother, built up over years spent in the boring routines of lifting weights and running on treadmills. She could never see the point herself, but he loved it. Hour upon hour of a single-minded obsession with his own body. Never mind, his strength would serve now.

'Don't forget to wear the gear.' She pointed to two pairs of plastic gloves and a cheap plastic windcheater she had bought in Sainsbury's a few days ago. 'We mustn't leave any trace of ourselves.'

He put on the gloves and the windcheater, then dragged the body to the open door, pulling it forward and lifting it across his shoulder.

'Not very heavy, I could take two of him.'

'Place him sitting against the monument.'

He obeyed her. He always obeyed her. They were re-united a year ago after being separated for years. It was a shame about the other one. He had got cold feet just when they were about to start. A combination of the old woman and his time in jail had got to him, making him weak and fearful. He had threatened to expose them. She couldn't allow it to happen.

She looked down at Phil Marsland sitting upright against the monument. 'He won't fall over?'

'Nah, he'll stay right where he is.'

'Good, just what I want.' She reached out and brushed Phil's hair with her gloved hand, making it look neat and tidy. Phil Marsland taking a last look at the world through dead eyes.

Shame about him, a pretty boy. But like the others, he had to die.

It was all part of the plan.

'Time for you to drop me close to home,' she told her brother. Their job was done today.

Now all they had to do was wait for the shit to hit the fan.

## Chapter Thirty-Three

'I'm sorry, I thought the decision was the best for the Coroner's Office.' Margaret Challinor pushed a long grey hair away from her eyes.

'Without talking to me first?'

'There wasn't time. It was an offer from Claire Trent. I had to make a decision quickly.'

'So now you've put me in the position of liaising with a family and reporting on them at the same time.'

'As I said, it was a quick decision.' She sat back in her chair and stared at him. 'Look, we have an opportunity to rebuild bridges with MIT here. They have a new boss in charge…'

'A woman who you know…'

'A woman who I know and admire. To get where she has in the police force has taken intelligence, perseverance and acumen.'

'It's also taken ruthlessness, the ability to use people and sod the consequences.'

'All attributes that would make her an attractive friend to my department and a difficult enemy.'

'But you put me in an impossible position.'

'I don't have to remind you DI Ridpath, you are a serving police officer.'

'Do you think I could forget? GMP is a hierarchical organisation. Once you are out of the hierarchy you are incredibly weak. People start to make decisions for you rather than with you.'

She turned and stared out of the large sash window to her right. 'It's also an incredible strength, Ridpath. Use it.'

'Hard when people are taking decisions for me.'

'Listen to me. It was necessary. We need to improve our relations with MIT. Trust me, when I say it's part of a bigger plan.'

'So I'm just another cog in the power game?'

'No, Ridpath, far more important. You are a valuable member of my team.'

He stood up. 'Then treat me like I am not just another pawn on a bloody chess board.'

He walked out, leaving her sitting behind her desk. He was beyond angry. She talked a good game about empowerment and inclusivity – all the management speak he had heard on his training courses – but in the end, she was just like all the rest of them. At least with Charlie Whitworth you knew where you stood. You were either in or out. At the moment, Ridpath was the pig in the middle and he didn't like it one little bit.

# Chapter Thirty-Four

Ridpath sat down at his desk and took three deep breaths. He hated being controlled and manipulated, even by somebody like Margaret Challinor. He recognised the contradictions in his behaviour. After all, any uniformed service was all about taking orders and doing what you were told, wasn't it? But in the police it had never felt that way. He was always a part of a team, doing what was right for the case.

Not playing politics.

Not letting egos get in the way.

Not playing silly buggers.

It was all about gathering enough evidence to put the criminal away. That was it. The evidence was king, nothing and nobody else mattered.

He stared at his to-do list. For the first time it stretched over two pages. The first line read.

*Check on coroner's report for Ronald Wilson.*

A shiver went down his back and he coughed. He suddenly felt cold. Dr Morris had said to avoid stress and here he was as tense as a scalded cat after the confrontation with Margaret Challinor.

Take three breaths and calm down, Ridpath.

For once he listened to himself. He inhaled deeply and held it. There, he was feeling better already. Still angry but feeling better about it.

Later, he would have to meet Michael Connelly and his family, something he was not looking forward to. His mind flashed back six years to the last time he had seen Connelly. The man's body bent double and his hands forced behind his back, handcuffs being placed on his wrists by Charlie Whitworth. It was a dawn raid on Connelly's unobtrusive semi in a quiet cul-de-sac of Eccles. He hadn't tried to resist at all, just smiled as Dave Hardy read him his rights, charging him with armed robbery.

'I'll be out by lunchtime,' was all he said. And he was. The case was dropped by CPS six months later as witnesses miraculously discovered they could not remember anything about the incident. Even the post office manager who had stared down the barrel of a sawn-off shotgun suddenly acquired a bad case of amnesia.

Intimidation. Extortion. Racketeering. All Connelly family values, and he would have to deal with them as well as report back to Claire Trent.

A shiver went down his spine again. Enough. Focus on work, Ridpath.

He picked up the phone and dialled the number for the pathology department at Manchester Royal Infirmary. He was put through to an answering machine.

'You've reached Dr James Schofield. I'm either in the lab, performing a post-mortem or sleeping. Either way, I don't want to be disturbed. But if you leave your name and number after the beep, I'll get back to you just as soon as I can.'

On a machine the voice sounded higher and more youthful, like a teenager pretending to be an adult. Ridpath left a message. 'Hello Dr Schofield, this is DI Ridpath from the Coroner's Office. Just a couple of questions. When will I be able to see the post-mortem report on Ronald Wilson? Secondly, do we have a date for the release of Gerard Connelly's body? I need to meet with the family this afternoon. If you could get back to me before then it would be appreciated. Thank you.'

He looked at the list again. Only forty-three things left to do. He leant back, cracked his knuckles and started on number three; the death of a Mr Robert Hampson, aged seventy-eight.

By two o'clock he had crossed off twenty-seven of the items on his list. If he was free tomorrow he would come in for a couple of hours to finish the rest.

Ridpath hated to leave things undone, and with Polly and Eve still living at her mother's, there was little to do at home except look at the four walls or watch telly. During his illness he had spent hours inside either pre-chemo or post chemo, with only the telly for company. He'd had enough of *Cash in the Attic* or bloody *Homes in the Country* to last him this lifetime and the next.

He'd do anything to avoid staying at home again.

Even go to see one of Manchester's biggest thugs on a Saturday afternoon. He checked the man's home address in the file. Time to get on with it.

## Chapter Thirty-Five

The taxi company was housed in a small Nissen hut on the outskirts of a rundown council estate.

He'd been sent here after first calling on the unobtrusive semi-detached house that served as the Connelly home. A young woman in her twenties had answered the door. She'd obviously been crying. After showing her his coroner's officer ID card, she answered his question.

'He's not here.'

'I need to see him about Gerard Connelly. Could you tell me where he is?'

At the mention of her brother's name, her eyes moistened again. 'Where he always is. Down the taxi office.'

'Perhaps I could speak to your mother.'

'That'd be hard.'

'Why?'

'She died four years ago.' The eyes of the young woman filled with tears again.

'I'm sorry for your loss.' Ridpath always found the mouthing of these platitudes difficult. For him, when they came out of his mouth it always sounded so insincere. What he should say rather than what he really felt. The course had spent a whole day on grief and family counselling, particularly on how to express empathy correctly. He still found it difficult though, the words always got in the way.

'Yeah, so am I,' she finally answered.

'Could you tell me where the taxi firm is?'

She pointed down to the end of the street. 'Just turn right and you'll see it on the left. Cars will be parked outside with the name Carmen on them.'

Ridpath smiled. 'An original name for a taxi firm,' he said ironically.

'My dad named it after my mother. Carmen Sheehan.'

Ridpath kicked himself. Rule number one, never make assumptions. He tried to recover his discomfort. 'Is there anything I can do for you at this terrible time?'

She appeared to think for a moment. 'Yeah, there is something…'

'What's that?'

'Bugger off and leave me alone, copper.'

The door slammed in his face, the glass still vibrating as he stood there.

That was well handled, Ridpath. A sudden craving for the comfort of a cigarette washed over him. He resisted the urge, striding away from the house in the direction she had pointed.

The street was quiet, peaceful. Classic suburbia; houses built in the 1930s out of red brick, net curtains covering the windows. Vauxhalls, Toyotas and Fords in the driveways, neatly tended rose-filled gardens in front.

Who'd have thought one of Manchester's biggest criminals lived here?

At the end of the street, on the other side of the road, an old Nissen hut stood in a patch of open ground on the edge of a park. Outside the hut a variety of cars, all sporting the logo of Carmen Taxis were illegally parked on the grass verge.

Carmen Taxis. Michael Connelly's late wife's name. Ridpath felt his face redden at the mistake.

'Should have kept my mouth shut,' he said out loud to himself.

Ridpath walked up the short concrete path and rapped on the door. A well-built man answered. He was the caricature of the film heavy; bald head, broken nose and bulging muscles encased in a dark leather jacket, like a human black pudding.

'What you wan'?'

'I'm here to see Michael Connelly.'

'He ain't seeing nobody.' The thug went to close the door. Ridpath stuck his foot in the gap.

'I'm from the Coroner's Office. I need to see him regarding his son.'

From inside a voice called out weakly. 'Let him in, Pat.'

Michael Connelly was sitting behind an old wooden desk. In front of him family photos were strewn across the top. The rest of the cabin was a mess; old Pirelli calendars on the wall, a faded picture of the queen, three Union Jacks and metal filing cabinet filled the far wall. The rest of the space was occupied by a dishevelled job-lot of sofas, chairs and stools Oxfam had rejected as being unsuitable for use.

Michael Connelly looked up from the photo he was holding. His eyes were red and rheumy, his face round and blotched, a tracing of red veins sprouting on the cheeks. 'Now's not the right time.'

Ridpath looked for somewhere to sit down. He moved a pile of old *Sun* newspapers off a chair and onto the floor.

'Didn't you hear me, I said now is not the right time.'

The thug called Pat took one step forward menacingly.

Ridpath stared at him forcing him to stop. He turned back to Michael Connelly. 'I'm here about your son, Gerard.'

The man leant forward. 'Speak but make it quick.'

'I'm from the Coroner's Office Your son has been examined by the pathologist and we are just waiting on his report before we can release the body back to you.'

'You've cut my son up?'

'In all cases of suspicious deaths, the coroner will always request a post-mortem.'

The small eyes narrowed. 'A suspicious death? I thought Gerard was run over in a car accident...'

'He was, but...'

'But?'

Ridpath took a deep breath. The man was going to find out anyway, better it came from him. 'There were suspicious circumstances...'

'Like being chased by a man armed with a gun?'

It was Ridpath's turn to be surprised,. 'How did you...?'

'A little bird in GMP told me. He was on the phone to me even before Charlie Whitworth arrived with his cock and bull story about a traffic accident. I wanted to see if you'd tell me more lies.'

'Not the way I work.'

'Then tell me the truth of what happened.'

Ridpath took a deep breath. 'We believe he was being chased at the time of his death.'

The man lurched forward. 'Chased? Chased by who?'

'We don't know. That's what we're trying to find out.'

'We? I thought you said you were a coroner's officer?'

'I'm on temporary secondment from GMP. It's DI Ridpath in case you wanted to know.'

The piggy eyes narrowed again. 'We've met before?'

'Possibly...'

A long fat finger with a dirty nail pointed at Ridpath's face. 'I remember you. Part of Charlie Whitworth's mob, ain't you?'

'Not any more, on assignment to the coroner.'

Michael Connelly chuckled. 'They put you out to grass?'

Ridpath didn't answer as the door opened and a man stepped into the cabin, bumping fists with the thug at the door. He looked the spitting image of Gerard Connelly. Again, Ridpath flashed back to the face through his windscreen, hands resting on the bonnet of his car, chest struggling for breath, blue eyes staring wildly, the angel's wings fluttering...

'Who's this? The young man asked.'

'This is... what's your bloody name again?'

'I'm the coroner's officer, DI Ridpath.'

'You a copper?'

Michael Connelly answered for him. 'Sort of. They've retired him. Used to be with Charlie Whitworth.'

'What's he doing here?'

'Let's ask him, shall we?'

This was obviously a game, played between the two of them. A power game, with him as the sacrificial pawn. 'Now we've worked out who I am, who are you?' asked Ridpath.

Again Michael Connelly answered as another set of blue eyes bored into Ridpath's skull. 'This is Graham, my eldest, Gerard's brother.'

'Why are you here?' repeated Graham.

'As I was explaining to your father, after the pathologist has completed his report the body of your brother will be returned to the family for burial. I'm here to sort out the paperwork.'

'We want Gerard now.'

'I'm afraid that's impossible. The pathologist hasn't...'

Graham Connelly was standing over Ridpath in a flash. His face inches away. 'You're not listening to me. We want my brother back... now.'

Ridpath didn't flinch. 'And you're not listening to me. He will be released when the coroner says so, not before. In a suspicious death...'

'You've said that before. How do you know it was suspicious?' asked Michael Connelly.

The young man blinked and stood upright.

Ridpath took a deep breath. Michael Connelly was going to find out the details anyway from his mole. Better he heard it from the horse's mouth. 'Because I was there when it happened.'

'What... what are you saying?'

'I was driving back from Teesside. Your son ran across the road in front of my car. I was able to stop in time, but the lorry driver couldn't.'

'We gonna do for that lorry driver...' said Graham.

Michael held up his hand, silencing his son. 'You're not telling us everything,'

'I saw a man with a gun, chasing your son.'

Graham Connelly was in his face again. 'Who? Who did you see?'

'I don't know. If I did, we would have him under arrest.'

'It doesn't matter, copper, we'll find him before you and when we do, his life isn't going to be worth living.'

'Leave it to us. We'll find out who did it.'

'This copper hasn't worked it out, Dad.'

'Mr Coroner's Officer, we sort out our own problems. We will find out who killed Gerard and we will deal with it ourselves.'

'Even if innocent people get hurt in the process?'

It was Graham who answered. 'You police may control the day, but when the lights go down and you go home to your suburban homes or eat doughnuts in the quiet of your nick, that's when we come out. This is Manchester. We own the night and we sort out our problems. We don't need coppers, or judges or courts. All we need is ourselves alone.'

'And all you'll do is create another gang war like there was back in ninety-nine. Guns on the streets, people getting shot, a child dying.'

'We don't want no gang war, Ridpath. Why would we? Everyone is making money and there hasn't been trouble for years. But I'll tell you this for nothing, if somebody was chasing Gerard and caused his death, they and the rest of their mob will pay with their lives.'

'Gunchester again?'

Graham Connelly laughed. 'That was then, this is now. That was run by some crazy Yardies, not us. We have more soldiers than the police. And we can put more guns on the ground than you. Don't take us on Mr Policeman. You're going to lose.'

Ridpath stood up. 'Like I said, I'll call you when your son's body is released by the pathologist. Do you have an undertaker?'

Michael Connelly nodded. 'O'Casey. He handles the big Manchester funerals.'

'Looks like he's going to be a busy man over the next few weeks,' said Graham.

'Leave it to us, Mr Connelly.'

Michael shook his head. 'We need no help, we'll sort it out ourselves.'

Ridpath walked to the door. The black pudding thug stepped out of his way.

Just as he was about to exit, Michael Connelly raised his voice. 'Don't get in our way, Mr Coroner's Officer. If you do, you will regret it.'

'The only thing I regret is not putting you and your family away years ago.'

Ridpath slammed the door behind him. The wooden cabin seemed to rattle on its foundations.

As he walked away his phone rang. It was Charlie Whitworth.

'We just got a call from Stretford nick. The driver of the car on the M60 just walked in.'

## Chapter Thirty-Six

Charlie Whitworth stood in front of the two-way mirror.

Ridpath entered the viewing room and walked across to stand beside him. Through the glass he could see a middle-aged Asian man with three days of beard sprouting in chaotic profusion. The bags under the man's eyes were deep and sagging and his eyes were red-veined.

'Thanks for calling, Charlie.'

'It's more than you deserve, Ridpath.' He turned back to talk to a young DS standing at the back of the room in the shadows. 'How long's he been sitting there?'

'About an hour, boss. We called you as soon as we worked out who he was. He's been cooking here nicely while we waited for you to come.' The DS at Stretford was obviously newly promoted. He was deferential to Charlie Whitworth to the point of obsequiousness. 'His name's Abdul Qadir. Runs a newsagents cum-corner shop cum-offy. Been done twice for dodgy cigarettes.'

'Dodgy or no tax?' asked Ridpath trying to understand whether the man was making fake cigarettes or importing them from abroad.

'No tax. They had Arab stickers on them. Apparently fags are as cheap as chips in Dubai.'

'Have you seen the price of a packet of chips, recently?' grumbled Whitworth.

The DS had the sense to keep silent.

'Where's the car?'

'In the car park out front. Apparently, the stupid bugger drove it here. No tax, no insurance and false plates.'

'So he's stuffed?'

'Looks like it.'

Charlie Whitworth thought for a moment. 'Can you run the interview? I want myself and DI Ridpath here to have a watching brief.'

'No problem, boss. I reckon he's cooked long enough, don't you?'

'Just get on with it,' Whitworth said cruelly.

The detective sergeant left the room and three seconds later entered the room next door, accompanied by a young, pretty woman dressed in civvies. The Asian man raised his head and shifted nervously in his seat.

The woman sat down and started the recording machine. Immediately the sound of their voices came through clearly from speakers mounted on the wall.

'Good afternoon, Mr Qadir, my name is Detective Sergeant Harrison and this is DC Kate Walsh.'

Charlie sighed loudly. 'His name is Ian Harrison, his rank is detective sergeant. What are they teaching them in training school these days?'

The voices continued through the speakers. 'The time is now 12:23 p.m. on Saturday, April 21st, 2018. We are interviewing Mr Abdul Qadir, who has waived his right to have a solicitor present at this interview. If you could state your name, age and address for the tape.'

The Asian man leant forward to speak directly into the machine. Ridpath expected the voice to be heavily accented when he spoke. And it was. But the sound was a pure Manchester whine not the voice of Pakistan.

'My name is Abdul Qadir, innit. I'm thirty-seven years old and I live at 27 Hardie Street, Old Trafford.'

'Thank you, Mr Qadir. Can you tell us in your own words why you have come to the station this afternoon?'

At least Ian Harrison knew what he was doing. The opening question was open-ended, classic interviewing technique.

'I saw the article in the paper, didn't I?'

'Which article in which paper?'

'The article in the *Evening News* about the accident on Wednesday night on the M60.'

DS Harrison stayed silent. Another classic technique. He had learned his lessons carefully.

'You know, the accident where the man was killed and all the traffic was blocked for hours. It was on the BBC, weren't it?'

'So you saw the accident?'

Abdul Qadir shook his head. 'No, but the police want to interview the man driving a white car. That was me,' he said pointing to his nose.

'So you were the driver of the white car with the number plate P368 CWS?'

'Yeah, I just said that.'

DS Harrison had just ensured the man admitted to driving the car with false number plates. If he also had no tax or insurance they would throw the book at him. But Ridpath wished he would concentrate on the accident not grabbing another conviction to help the stats.

As if by telepathy Harrison seemed to hear him. 'Tell us about the accident, Mr Qadir, what did you see?'

'Well, I didn't see the accident itself because I'd already driven past.'

'So what did you see?'

Great, still neutral questions. Harrison was good at his job. Even Charlie was quiet now, listening intently.

'Well, I was driving to see my friend, Ali Mohammed; he runs a shop in Hyde. Very good shop, turnover more than a hundred thousand quid a year, next to a housing estate, you see, great location.'

'But what did you see before the accident, Mr Qadir?' It was the female DC who spoke, trying to keep her witness on track.

'Well, I was driving along when this naked white guy suddenly ran across the road in front of me. He came out of nowhere. So I slammed on my brakes but I thought I wasn't going to stop in time so I swerved onto the hard shoulder to avoid him.' All the time he was speaking, Abdul Qadir was holding his arms in front of him as if gripping an imaginary steering wheel.

'What did the man look like, Mr Qadir?' Harrison was back asking the questions again.

'Dunno really, it all happened so fast. He was white and he had no clothes on. I tell a lie. He was wearing a pair of boxers.'

'What colour were they?'

A frown appeared on Abdul Qadir's forehead as he thought of the answer. 'Blue, they were blue.'

'Good, Mr Qadir. Can you tell us did you see anybody else on the road?'

Ridpath sat forward. For him, this was the key question.

'Somebody else?'

'Yes, another person?'

Abdul Qadir shook his head. 'There was nobody on the road, only the naked white guy. Like I said, he just ran straight in front of me. I nearly hit him.'

Ridpath sat back and sighed. He had seen somebody that day, hadn't he? Why had nobody else seen the man with the gun?

Inside the interview room, DS Harrison was speaking. '...Do you have a dash cam in your car?'

'Abdul Qadir laughed. 'In that old tin can? There'd be no point. Only cost me a hundred and fifty quid.'

Charlie Whitworth turned to Ridpath. 'He didn't see anybody and there's no footage. You're screwed.'

Ridpath held his head in his hands. Somebody must have seen the man. He can't have been the only one.

Inside the interview room, DS Harrison was now asking questions about the ownership of the car. 'You are aware your car has false number plates?'

Abdul Qadir held his hands up. 'I don't know nothing about that. Bought it from a man in a pub, said he needed the money urgently.'

'You didn't transfer ownership through the DVLA in Swansea. You have to notify the vehicle authorities if a car is bought or sold.'

'I'm just a poor shop owner, I don't know nothing about rules and regulations...'

Charlie Whitworth nudged Ridpath's arm. 'Time for us to go. It's Saturday afternoon, and I need to check on the surveillance guys watching Michael Connelly.'

Then it hit Ridpath. He jumped up out of his seat and ran next door, bursting into the room as Abdul Qadir was explaining about his lack of licence and insurance.

Both Harrison and Walsh stared at the him. 'I just need to ask one question,' he muttered.

Harrison nodded to Walsh. She leant forward towards the recording machine and said, 'Detective Inspector Ridpath has just entered the room.'

Ridpath smiled at the witness. His voice was soft and emollient. 'Mr Qadir, you said you saw nobody on the road, only the white male.'

'That's correct.'

'Did you see anybody at the side of the road?'

'Do you mean not on the motorway or the hard shoulder?' Ridpath nodded.

A slow smile crept across Abdul Qadir's lips as he saw the detectives waiting for the answer. 'I don't know. The stress of knowing if I'm going to be charged with owning a car with the wrong plates has made me forgetful.'

'I'm sure if you're honest with us, DS Harrison will be able to take your honesty into account before he makes a decision on the charges. Won't you DS Harrison?'

'Of course, I will. A witness's honesty is always important to me.'

Abdul Qadir spent a few moments weighing up his answer, then he nodded his head. 'I did see somebody at the side of the road. Not for long though. It was when I swerved around the naked man, I saw him out of the corner of my eye.'

'What was he wearing?'

'A grey hoodie and jeans. He was standing near the fence at the side of the road.'

'Did you see his face?'

Abdul Qadir shook his head. 'It was covered by his hoodie.'

'Was he holding anything?'

The Asian man thought for a moment and then shook his head again. 'He may have been, but it all happened so quickly, I'm not sure.'

'Thank you, Mr Qadir.'

'I've told you what I know. Are you still going to charge me?'

Ridpath shrugged his shoulders. 'That's up to DS Harrison. Nothing to do with me, I'm afraid.'

Ridpath left the room as DS Harrison began to speak to the witness. 'As you have been co-operative and surrendered to the police voluntarily...'

## Chapter Thirty-Seven

Ridpath and his boss walked back to their cars, not talking to each other but smoking their own brands of cigarette.

On their left the giant telephone box that was old Stretford Town Hall loomed over them. Across the road Lancashire County Cricket ground was silent as the cricket season was in its early stages and the team were playing somewhere else. Even the roads were quiet; not jammed with the thousands of football fans on their way to the match at the Stadium of Dreams just down the road.

Finally Charlie spoke. 'Looks like you've been vindicated, Ridpath. There was another man there.'

'And the man was chasing Gerard Connelly, that's why he ran across the M60.'

A quiet puff of the Embassy followed by the expellation of smoke through the nostrils. Filtered by the moustache, it rose to halo Charlie's head.

Saint Charlie Whitworth, thought Ridpath, nothing could been further from the truth.

'Aye, but still no confirmation of the gun.'

'Jesus, Charlie, what do I need to do? I tell you I saw a gun in the man's hand. He was going to shoot Gerard, but Connelly was hit by the lorry.'

'I'll let ma'am know we've got confirmation.' He chuckled to himself. 'Now she's going to have to change her story again.'

'Why do you enjoy winding her up, Charlie? You're just going to create trouble for yourself.'

'There's got to be some perks from this job, Ridpath. And seeing Ms Trent's knickers in a twist is one of mine.' Then he stared at Ridpath. 'You're not defending her, are you?'

'She's a good copper, Charlie, who'd be an even better guvnor if you let her.'

'You are protecting her.' His eyes narrowed. 'What happened between you two on the course? Did you give her one?'

Ridpath stepped back. 'You know me, Charlie, I've loved Polly from day one. Never been unfaithful to her. Ever.' Ridpath neglected to mention that his night with Claire Trent happened before he met Polly. He crossed his fingers behind his back hoping Charlie wouldn't ask about the timings.

Instead, his boss pulled his nose, checking his fingers for any dirt. 'Whatever. It looks like we got a full on gang war on our hands. Plenty of overtime for the uniforms before this is over.' He took another drag of the Embassy. 'I wonder which lot it was. Salford, Cheetham Hill or Moss Side?'

'Could be a new mob we know nothing about,' suggested Ridpath.

'We're buggered if you're right.'

'It wouldn't surprise me. The state of our intelligence these days is woeful. They'd rather spend money once it's all kicked off, than try to stop it ever happening. Closing the community centres was the worst thing that ever happened. The gangs found a fertile recruiting ground amongst the estate kids.'

'My money is on Big Terry in Salford'

'Why?'

'I dunno, a copper's hunch. He's young and he's aggressive. Time to expand and where better than into Michael Connelly's territory?'

'But why knock off the youngest son. Surely, you'd go for the head of the snake, Connelly himself. It doesn't make sense.'

'Perhaps he wanted to put the fear of God into our Michael, let him know it's going to be him next.'

'And give him time to retaliate. Connelly and his son are not ones to take this lying down.'

DS Harrison appeared at the double doors of the building and waved to them. He ran across the car park. 'Thank God you're still here, they've found a body. It's Phil Marsland, Big Terry's son.'

## Chapter Thirty-Eight

Ridpath and Charlie Whitworth signed the sheet held by a constable at the entrance to the car park of All Saints Church. They ducked under the police tape surrounding the scene and walked towards the centre of activity, stopping just in front of more police tape forming the inner cordon.

Charlie went off to find Claire Trent. From where he stood Ridpath could see the naked body of Phil Marsland propped up in a sitting position leaning against a marble monument.

On the stone were carved the words:

*Marshall Stevens,*
*son of Sanders and Emma Stevens,*
*18 April 1852 – 12 August 1936*
*Whose life's work lies around this spot.*
*A founder of the Ship Canal*
*Manager of the Manchester Ship Canal Co.*
*Developer of Trafford Park*
*Member of Parliament for Eccles*

Some eminent Victorian, no doubt. One of those people who had created the city and now lay here long forgotten.

Surrounding the memorial was a phalanx of white coated SOCO's with a pathologist, Protheroe this time, bent over examining the body closely. It looked to Ridpath like a mannequin on display in a department store, one whose clothes had not been put on yet.

Off to the left an investigation of detectives stood around, waiting for permission to come forward. At the centre were

Claire Trent and Charlie Whitworth, worried looks on both their faces.

Unlike the middle of the M60, this crime scene was relatively easy to control, being in the grounds of a former Roman Catholic church. The church wasn't used any more, but was still well looked after. A sign behind him proudly proclaimed it was in the care of the Greyfriars monks of London as it was the finest example in the country of one of Pugin's Gothic Revival Churches.

To Ridpath it looked dark and menacing, designed to impress its congregation with the power of the church rather than welcome them in to worship. He remembered his own brush with Catholicism in the shape of a large, bald priest called Father Newman who took perverse delight in hitting young boys who couldn't remember their catechism.

Bastard.

The church was in a strange position, with no houses surrounding it. Instead, it was on its own next to the Ship Canal.

Behind him, the dome of the Trafford Centre stood out like a beacon of trade and consumerism. To the left, the constant drone of traffic on the M60 and the cantilevered slope of the Chill Factor, an indoor skiing centre. To the right, the once proud factories of Trafford Park, now mostly abandoned or turned into retail parks. In front of him, the Manchester Ship Canal and Barton Swing Bridge. Across the bridge lay Eccles, a once prosperous but now tired post-industrial town, famous for just one thing. A pastry with raisins.

Was the location significant? Here where Manchester, Eccles and Salford met. Was the person who killed Big Terry's son sending a message?

He looked back at the church. Nobody came here any more, there was no congregation, a perfect place to dump a body.

The semi-naked corpse was still leaning on the monument, the white flesh stark in the cold light of a Manchester spring. 'April is the cruellest month'. The words came back to him spoken in the voice of the Dominican teacher at his school. Another bastard, but one who loved English Lit. He would ask Polly later who had written it, she was bound to know.

And then he remembered he wouldn't be seeing Polly later. Or Eve. A wave of sadness washed over his body, drowning him in its hurt.

Pull yourself together Ridpath.

He walked over to join the detectives. Charlie Whitworth acknowledged his arrival, but Claire Trent ignored him. His DCI must have already told her the news about Abdul Qadir.

Ridpath glanced back at the naked body, now shielded from view by the white-suited pathologist and another SOCO. 'How do we know it's Big Terry's son?'

'One of the uniforms recognised him. Pulled him in a couple of years ago for possession,' answered Charlie.

'Cocaine or heroin?'

'A lump of dope. The magistrate let him off with a small fine and a slap on the wrist. Hardly worth the bother.'

Claire Trent glanced up at him. 'What are you doing here, Ridpath?'

'I brought him,' said Charlie, 'he's the coroner's eyes and ears. Also, we can do with every man we've got at the moment.'

Charlie blushed as he realised what he had just said to his senior officer. '…And woman too, of course,' he stammered.

Claire Trent ignored him. 'You've met Michael Connelly?'

'Got the phone call from Charlie as I was leaving him. He's spitting fire about the death of his son.'

'Looks like he's already started getting revenge, didn't wait long,' said Charlie.

'I don't think so. He's too upset over Gerard Connelly's death. Hasn't left his taxi shed since the news according to the daughter.'

'He could have ordered the killing.'

Ridpath remembered Graham Connelly coming in to the shed after he had arrived. 'I met the eldest son. Nasty piece of work.'

'You don't know half of it,' said Charlie.

The pathologist stood up, stared at the body one last time as if saying a prayer, and walked towards them, pulling the Tyvex mask and hood away from his face. 'I've just pronounced him dead at 5:35 p.m.'

'You don't need a bloody degree to work that one out,' said Charlie.

Protheroe stared at him. 'But I have one and it allows me to make that determination, Chief Inspector. You, on the other hand, don't and couldn't.'

Claire Trent was becoming visibly annoyed by the bickering. 'Get a grip both of you. This isn't some petty playground squabble, a man is lying dead over there.' She pointed back towards the monument. The scene of crime team were erecting a white tent over it, shielding the body from view.

Charlie nodded once and looked away. Dr Protheroe stood his ground, the muscle at the side of his face twitching beneath the unshaven cheeks.

'What can you tell us, doctor?'

'It's early days and I'll know more when I take the body back for a complete post-mortem. Death appears to be from a single gunshot wound to the right temple, the bullet exiting just below the left ear. Death would have been instantaneous.'

'Self-inflicted?' asked Claire Trent.'

The pathologist shook his head. 'Not a chance, unless he held a gun with his toes. The hands were tied behind his back. Additionally, the body displays cuts and burn marks made before he died.'

'He was tortured?' said Claire Trent.

'I believe so, but once again, these are observational findings only. Please wait for my full report after the post-mortem.'

'It looks like it's on display, propped up against the monument,' said Charlie.

Claire Trent ignored the observation, asking the pathologist, 'Time of death?'

'I've checked his body with a rectal thermometer and I would estimate he died between six and eight hours ago.'

'So around ten o'clock?'

The pathologist nodded. 'I also believe he wasn't killed here.'

'How do you know?' asked Charlie.

'In layman's terms, there are inconsistencies in the pathology that rule out this area as the place of death.'

'Such as?' Charlie pressed him.

'Again in layman's terms, the body shows signs of having lain on its left side for a considerable time before it was placed in a sitting position. Additionally, there is a complete absence of blood or brain matter on the ground around the body, suggesting he was killed elsewhere and then placed here.'

Ridpath jumped in. 'How long did the body lie on its side before it was moved?'

'A good question, DI Ridpath. The lividity suggest something in the region of two hours, but again please do not quote me.'

'Thank you, doctor. That's really useful.'

Charlie Whitworth stared at him. 'Why? Why is it useful?'

'Because it means if the body was killed around ten o'clock and then lay on its side for two hours, the earliest he could have been placed here was noon.'

'That would be my best estimate.' The doctor glanced over his shoulder, pulling his Tyvex hood back over his head. The SOCOs had finished erecting the tent. 'Time to finish my preliminary examination.' He turned to walk away, stopping for a second and then turning back. 'One more thing, his penis was removed after death. We can't find it anywhere near the body.'

There was a collective intake of breath from the assembled male detectives.

Before Ridpath could ask another question, a shout erupted from the direction of the main road.

'Let me see him. I want to see him.'

Ridpath, Claire Trent and the rest of the detectives ran towards the commotion.

A large bald-headed man with a bright blue tattoo of a spider's web on his neck was struggling with two sergeants and a constable.

'I want to see him He's my son, let me see him.'

'Terry, calm down. You know we can't let you into the crime scene,' Claire Trent shouted.

'But he's my son, you bastards. I've gotta see him.'

More cars were screeching to a halt on the road outside the church. The doors swung open and more thugs piled out, advancing towards the thin blue line of policemen guarding the outer cordon. In the front of the thugs was a blonde-haired woman who seemed to be their leader.

'Steve, get on to HQ and request back-up immediately from the tactical unit. Make it a priority.'

The DC who drove her around, shouted 'yes, guvnor,' and ran back to where his car was parked.

The new thugs arrived in force and immediately pulled their boss away from the uniformed coppers and began to push their way through the cordon. The blonde-haired woman stood next to her father, clenching and unclenching her fists.

Ridpath and Charlie Whitworth joined the ranks and pushed back. Ridpath found himself head to head with a thug with a buzz cut and a livid cut over his left eye. He stank of BO.

More cars arrived, each full of young men.

Ridpath felt his arm being gripped by Charlie Whitworth as the pressure against his body increased. On his other side was Catherine Delaney, the newest member of MIT, an aggressive and determined look in her eyes.

But despite this, the police line was being forced backwards.

Luckily the entrance to the church was only twelve feet wide, bordered on either side by a brick wall and a privet hedge. Still more thugs arrived. Ridpath felt himself being forced backwards, the BO of the thug in front of him heavy in his nostrils.

Ridpath heard Claire Trent's voice behind him as the new arrivals joined the crowd and began to push against the cordon.

'Is the church open?'

'Yes, ma'am,' one of the sergeants answered, his voice muffled as his hat fell off and was trampled by the onrushing trainers of the gang.

She shouted, louder this time, her voice aimed at the bald-headed man at the centre of the action. 'Listen, Terry, go and wait in the church. We'll let you see your son when the pathologist has finished examining the body.'

Big Terry stopped struggling with the two sergeants. 'He's my son. I have to be able to see him.'

'You'll see him when the pathologist has finished, that's a promise.'

'You can't do that, ma'am. Chain of evidence,' shouted Charlie, pushing a thug back with his forearm to the man's throat.

'Don't tell me what I can or can't do, DCI Whitworth,' she said through gritted teeth. 'You wait in the church, Terry, we'll tell you when you can see him.'

Terry used his elbows to create a free space around him. 'Stop it you lot. Stop it.'

The rest of the pushing and shoving from the gang members gradually ceased, except for Catherine Delaney and a young thug who were still eyeball to eyeball, their foreheads seemingly joined like Siamese twins.

'Pull them apart,' ordered Claire Trent. 'And when you've finished, help me show Mr Marsland to the church.'

'Yes, ma'am' said one of the sergeants, separating the two combatants.

'I'm Tracy and I'm going in with my dad, it's my brother over there.'

Big Terry and his daughter were allowed through the cordon and were taken to the church by Claire Trent.

As they walked away, two police vans arrived outside the church and coppers dressed in riot gear piled out of the back.

They formed up and marched up the road, placing themselves between the crowd and the cordon. The crowd began an ironic whistling of the Laurel and Hardy tune – dee-dum, dee-dum, de-dum, dee-dee, diddly-dum, diddly-dee, dee-dum…

Five minutes later Claire Trent came out of the church and shouted across the car park, 'MIT detectives to me.'

# Chapter Thirty-Nine

She gathered her team around her out of hearing of the crowd.

'Listen, we're a gnat's dick away from a gang war. Alan, I want you to set up a command centre in the church. Keep everybody away from the area. Use whatever resources you need.'

The DS nodded his head. 'Yes, boss, what about Big Terry and his daughter?'

'Let him cool down in the church. We'll let him see his son before he's taken away but on no account is he to go closer than six feet, understand.'

'He's not going to be happy, boss.'

'Screw him and his happiness. We've got a murder here and nobody is going to contaminate the evidence. He told me he hadn't seen his son since he went out on Thursday night. He had a date with a woman apparently. Lorraine, find out from your surveillance team what Big Terry was up to around then and increase surveillance on his family.'

'Will do, boss, but I don't know if we have the manpower.'

'Well, find it. And it's personnel, not manpower, Lorraine.'

'Yes, boss.'

'Dave...'

Hardy put his hand up.

'Get on to the district commanders of all the South Manchester areas. I want a visible police presence on the streets for the next couple of days. Let the bastards know we're out there.'

'They're not going to be happy, boss, the overtime...'

'Sod the overtime, get the plods out from behind their desks and onto the streets. Tell them to call the chief constable and disturb his Saturday golf game if they want confirmation.'

'Yes, boss.'

'Sandra…'

One of the female detectives stepped forward.

'Good to have you on the team…'

Ridpath saw Charlie Whitworth's eyes roll upwards.

'…I want you to check all the CCTV in the area from noon to the time the body was discovered.'

'What am I looking for, guvnor.'

'I don't know. Unusual activity, any car parking near the church. There's no camera on the area the body was discovered but there are cameras on the church. Perhaps we'll get lucky and we'll see something.'

'Yes, guvnor.'

'And while you're at it, get somebody to take a statement from the man who found the body…'

'His name's Andy Turner. He's a maintenance worker, here to fix the cameras. Somebody smashed the lenses,' said Dave Hardy, 'he's waiting in the church.'

'Just our bloody luck. Get a statement from him and check them anyway. And keep him away from Big Terry, I don't want the circumstances of the death to get out.'

'Will do, guvnor.'

'Charlie, I want you to go and see Michael Connelly. Find out where he and his sons were at noon. Increase the surveillance but don't let him know he's being watched. I want to know his every move for the next couple of days. And get onto all your confidential informants, somebody must know who did this.'

'Yes, ma'am.'

'I don't think it was Connelly, boss.'

'Why, Ridpath? Come on, give us your coroner's officer wisdom.'

He ignored the put down. 'Like I said, boss, he was so caught up in his grief, I don't think he's had time to act.'

'What about the son, Graham?'

'When he talked, it was about getting revenge, not having taken it already. It's like they were still waiting for the old man to decide what to do. Just a hunch, boss, but I think it was somebody else.'

'Thanks for the wisdom, Ridpath, but I can't base the safety of the people of Manchester on one of your "hunches". You go with Charlie and keep him out of trouble.'

'But if I do, he'll definitely know I'm still with GMP.'

'So what? Charlie told me he clocked you already. No point in keeping up the game.'

'I don't need Ridpath, ma'am, I can handle Connelly with Dave Hardy.'

'Dave's doing something for me. Ridpath can be with you, that's an order.'

'Yes, ma'am.'

'Oh and one more thing, Charlie,' she said gently, 'that's the last time you question one of my decisions in front of the plods. Do I make myself clear?'

She stared at him waiting for an answer.

'Yes, ma'am,' Charlie finally said, his eyes burning into her.

'What are you going to do, guvnor?' asked Sandra.

'I'm going to have a chat with Big Terry, time to cut him down to size. So, what are you all waiting for, get a bloody move on.'

## Chapter Forty

The taxi shed was still there, beside the park. Except now there were four men standing outside it keeping watch. Obviously the word had already got out about the murder of Big Terry's son.

Charlie Whitworth stopped for a moment on the pavement, taking a surreptitious glance up at his men in the car down the road keeping the area under surveillance.

'We've got another team watching his house and one more checking on Graham Connelly's apartment in the northern district.' Charlie said out of the side of his mouth. 'They won't be able to fart without us knowing about it.'

'Are we up on their phones too?' asked Ridpath.

'The ones we know about, But this lot are smart, they'll be using burners, throwing them away every couple of weeks.'

'How long can we keep this up for Charlie?'

'The surveillance?'

Ridpath nodded.

'With extra manpower... sorry, personnel,' Charlie corrected himself, 'three, four days at most on all four gangs. Longer if we cut down on the scope of the surveillance. Anyway, let's get this over and done with.'

They walked down the short path and were immediately accosted by one of the men.

'What you wan'?'

'To speak to Michael Connelly.'

'Yeah, well he's not here.' The man's hand appeared on Charlie's chest. 'If you don't take your hand away in five seconds, I'll be arresting you for assaulting a police officer in the performance of his duty, section 89 paragraph one of the Police Act 1996.'

The man slowly removed his hand.

'Now get your boss.'

'Let him in, Toby,' a voice shouted from inside.

'Toby, your name is Toby?'

'What of it?'

'Another fucking mug, hey, Ridpath.'

'I thought that was a jug, Charlie.'

'Nah, this one's definitely a mug.'

The door opened and they stepped inside. Michael Connelly was sitting exactly where Ridpath had left him two hours ago. His eyes still red and moist. Graham Connelly was leaning on a cupboard to his left.

'Take a seat, Charlie. I see you've brought DI Ridpath with you. Left the Coroner's Office already, have we? Back with MIT? Has she kicked you out?'

'Who?' asked Ridpath.

'Mrs Challinor, heard she was a bit of a ball-breaker, doesn't like incompetent coppers.'

Charlie walked over to look at one of the old Pirelli calendars hanging on the wall. '1994. One of my favourites. 1996 is better though, draped over the F1 Cars.'

'Didn't know you were a connoisseur, Charlie.'

'I'm not, but everybody likes classic Pirelli. Shame they don't make them any more.'

'The world's changing around our ears, Charlie. Women won't stand for it. Take my daughter, calls herself a feminist she does. Wish she were more feminine, me, but she don't listen. Even had Carmen copying her before she passed on, rest her soul. World's changing, Charlie, me and you are the last dinosaurs.'

The DCI knocked papers off a chair with the back of his hand before sitting down. Ridpath remained standing.

'Where were you at noon, today?'

'Am I being interrogated, Charlie?'

'Nah, we're just having a friendly chat. So where were you?'

'We don't do friendly chats with coppers.'

Charlie switched his gaze to Graham Connelly. 'Nobody's talking to you, son… yet.' The gaze switched back to the father. 'So where were you?'

'Here.'

'And somebody can vouch for you?'

'At least twenty people.'

'And your son?'

'Here with me.'

'I suppose twenty people can vouch for him too.'

'No,' he shook his head, 'thirty can vouch for him.'

'Maybe more, Dad. I'd just come from Mass, remember?'

'Where did you go to church, All Saints?'

'Nah, St Hugh's. You can ask Father Devlin. A good friend is the good Father.'

'What Mr Whitworth was insinuating, Graham, with all the subtlety of a Manchester bus driven by a blind pensioner, was you are somehow involved in the death of Phil Marsland whose body has just been found at the church. You know the one, next to Barton Bridge.'

'That church? Never been there.'

Ridpath shook his head. How had Michael Connelly found out so quickly? They had only just been briefed an hour ago by Claire Trent.

'A little bird has told me Big Terry's son was found there. Right?'

Charlie Whitworth answered. 'I'm not at liberty to discuss an ongoing case. Where did you get your information?'

Michael Connelly glanced at his son and smiled, pulling out a newspaper and throwing it on the desk. In big, bold, black letters, the headline screamed 'GANG WAR.'

'Looks like you haven't been reading the papers recently.'

Beneath the headline, a grainy picture of a group of white-suited SOCOs around the monument obviously taken with a telephoto lens. Luckily, the body couldn't be seen.

Michael Connelly sat forward, his arms open in front of him. 'Listen, Charlie, I'll tell you this once and once only. We had nothing to do with the death of Big Terry's son. Jesus, aren't I after mourning my own son for the last couple of days. But I will tell you one thing. If it was Big Terry who killed Gerard, then his life won't be worth living, dead son or not.'

# Chapter Forty-One

'What do you think, Ridpath?'

They were walking away from the taxi shed, leaving behind Michael Connelly and his bodyguards.

'I know it's strange but I don't think he was involved in killing Phil Marsland.'

Charlie Whitworth was tugging furiously on one of his Embassies. For once, Ridpath hadn't joined him. He'd felt a tickle in the back of his throat, and his nose was stuffed, probably from too much smoking. Come to think of it, he hadn't noticed the smells in the hut, perhaps it was one of the side effects of the tablets he was taking.

'He's the obvious suspect. Revenge for his son.'

'But you heard him. He denied being involved.'

'Well, he would, wouldn't he? He's hardly likely to say "It's a fair cop, guvnor, it was me who shot Big Terry's son and cut off his todger".' Are you getting soft in your old age or has working for the coroner addled your brain? My money is on Michael Connelly or his son, probably bringing in some thug from Liverpool or Birmingham to do their dirty work.'

'But why, Charlie?'

'Revenge, Ridpath, the oldest motive in the book.'

'So Big Terry murdered Gerard Connelly and Michael killed Phil Marsland. A tit for tat killing?'

He took another drag on his cigarette. 'That's it, in a nutshell. All we have to do now is find the evidence to prove it and we can put both of the bastards away for a long, long time.' Charlie glanced at his watch. 'Shit, is that the time? I need to replace

Colin on the surveillance team looking at Graham Connelly's flat in the Northern Quarter. You got anything else to do?'

Ridpath thought of the cold, empty house waiting for him. He shook his head.

'Come on, you can keep me company and tell me why you don't think the two most murderous thugs in Manchester aren't trying to kill each other.'

The drive took less than thirty minutes. They parked in one of the city centre car parks and walked to Reston Street.

'You know, I remember when this was an area nobody gave a toss about; full of old pubs, drunks, druggies and hookers people wouldn't touch with a bargepole. Now look at it.'

To Ridpath the streets looked like they had always looked, but every shop was now a cafe serving avocado on toast, and designed with a job-lot of freshly distressed furniture. Inside, men with beards and women wearing black, chatted over achingly expensive artisan coffee.

Charlie began speaking again, the words coming out between drags on his Embassy. 'Funny thing is, there's more homeless living here than anywhere else. Come here after dark and virtually every doorway is occupied by a pile of dirty blankets with a body sucking on a can of Tennants Extra Strength beneath the covers. Somehow for our young inhabitants it adds to the "charm" of the place. Can't see it myself. Give me a quiet, tree-lined suburb any day of the week.' He stopped in front of a bright red door. 'We're in here on the second floor.'

Charlie pressed the intercom and a voice immediately answered. 'Who is it?

'Charlie.'

'About bloody time, boss.'

The door buzzed and they went in, climbing up two flights of stairs.

'How'd you get this place?'

'Claire Trent put the squeeze on one of the developers. You know the old "you scratch my back and we'll overlook your multiple infractions of fire and building regulations" number. Works every time.'

He knocked on the door and it was immediately opened by a detective called Colin Molesworth.

'Jesus, boss, you took your time. I was supposed to be off duty two hours ago.'

Charlie bustled in. 'You'll thank me for the overtime when you see your pay packet.'

The room was in darkness. A camera on a tripod was focused downwards through a hole in the curtain to the entrance to the flats. Another was focused horizontally. In the gloom Ridpath saw another detective with headphones on, next to a tape recorder. He walked over to the window. 'Anything?'

'Quiet as a City game. Nothing in or out. Nothing on tape either.'

The man with the headphones waved. 'Hi Charlie.'

'Ridpath, this is Grant Thornton from surveillance. Bugs R Us as we call them. If you ever need someone to spy on your wife, he's your man.'

Ridpath shook hands with the detective.

Colin Molesworth was already putting on his coat and bustling out of the door.

'You're on the Red Eye shift, Colin, don't be late.'

Molesworth nodded and then closed the door behind him.

Charlie bent down and checked both cameras before walking over to a table festooned with coffee cups and empty sandwich wrappers. 'Bloody Molesworth has eaten everything.'

Ridpath remembered long days following suspects. Hours spent in cars and apartments like these, where the only thing to do was eat bad junk food and drink worse coffee.

'I can go out and get something, Charlie.'

'Maybe later.'

Charlie sat down at the table and took out his cigarettes and lighter.

His face was illuminated by the flair of the lighter and a stream of smoke flowed from his mouth. 'Now why don't you think it was Michael Connelly?'

Same old Charlie, like a terrier with a rat once an idea had parked itself in his head.

Ridpath sat down next to him. 'Because it doesn't make sense. The four gangs had an agreement. They were all making money, why spoil it?'

'They are stupid thugs, Ridpath, shit doesn't have to make sense. You must have heard the story of the scorpion?'

Ridpath shook his head.

'A scorpion is walking through the desert when he spots a mouse in front of him. "I'm very tired, can you give me a lift to the top of the hill?" He asks the mouse. The mouse shakes his head. "If I let you climb on my back and take you there, you'll sting me with your tail." "I promise on my mother's life, I won't," the scorpion said. So the mouse shrugs his shoulders and allows the scorpion to climb on his back, racing away up the hill to the top. When they get there the scorpion raises his tail and stings the mouse on his head. As the mouse lies dying he asks the scorpion why he stung him. The scorpion answers "because that's who I am. It's what I do."'

Charlie Whitworth sat back with a smug smile on his face and took a long drag from his cigarette. 'It's what they do.'

'A cute story but it still doesn't answer me. There are reasons why Michael Connelly didn't do it.'

'Go on.

'Two things. First, I was with Michael Connelly and his son this afternoon. The way they were talking it was obvious they hadn't taken action yet.'

'They were just playing you,' Charlie sneered. 'I bet they remembered you were a copper the second you walked through the door. I told Claire Trent, Connelly wouldn't fall for it, but would she listen?' He shook his head. 'Cloth ears, that one.'

'Secondly, Big Terry said his boy was last seen on Thursday evening.'

'He had a date with some woman.'

'That means he vanished before we told Michael Connelly his son was dead.'

'But you're forgetting the age-old mantra of the detective.'

Ridpath stared at him wondering what was coming.

'What plus why equals who. The what was the shooting, the preferred method of Michael Connelly. The why was revenge for the death of his son. An eye for an eye. Put those two together and we get the who. Michael bloody Connelly and his family. All we have to do now is find the evidence.'

'We've got something happening,' said the detective from surveillance.

Charlie and Ridpath rushed to the side of the window.

'Down below them a van pulled up. Graham Connelly stepped out with his arm draped over the shoulders of a twelve-year-old, blond-haired boy. They were followed by an older, chubbier man dressed in a black track suit and trainers. The van drove off and, for a few moments, the three people stood on the pavement chatting. All the while, Graham Connelly was playing with the boy's hair.

'Shit, he's underage,' said Charlie. 'You heard the briefing, Graham Connelly has form for paedophilia and he's on the sex offenders' register.'

The three people were still standing on the street. Now, Graham Connelly and the young boy were play fighting. Connelly picked up the boy and lifted him over his shoulder, patting his bottom.

'You've got to do something, Charlie,' said Ridpath.

The two adults were talking now but Ridpath couldn't see what they were saying. The fat man pointed at the young boy.

Graham Connelly reached into his jacket, pulling out his wallet. Money was taken out and passed over to the fat man. Again something was said which Ridpath couldn't see. Then the fat man walked away, leaving Graham Connelly and the young boy together. They chatted for a moment, then

Connelly's arm went over the boy's shoulders and they walked to the entrance of the apartments.

'You have to do something Charlie, they're going inside.'

Charlie rushed to the Airwave radio on the desk. He pressed the send button. The machine squawked for a second before a male voice on the end of the line said, 'Comms here. Go ahead.'

'This is DCI Whitworth, can you patch me through to Detective Superintendent Trent?'

Ridpath saw Charlie's mobile phone lying on the desk next to him. Why didn't Charlie just call her on her mobile? He must have the number.

Comms answered. 'Just patching you through now, DCI Whitworth, hold on...'

A few more squawks and then it hit Ridpath. All communications on the Airwave were monitored and recorded. It was his way of ensuring the conversation was part of the record. Even now Charlie was thinking politically. At that moment Ridpath realised he never wanted to do Charlie's job, where every action was considered and evaluated for its political effect.

'You're through, DCI Whitworth.'

'Trent here, you got something for me, Charlie.'

'Not exactly, ma'am, we have a problem.'

The voice when it answered was slow and questioning without asking a question 'Go ahead...'

'We have just seen Graham Connelly entering his apartment in the Northern Quarter with a minor. A boy who can't be more than twelve years old.'

'So?'

'If you remember, ma'am, Graham Connelly was charged with sexual assault on a young boy.'

'I remember, Charlie.' There was a soft buzzing from the machine before Claire Trent's voice came on the other end of the line. 'But if we charge in there mob handed, Graham Connelly is going to know we are watching him. It will make it impossible for us to monitor his movements and conversations covertly any more.'

'But it's a twelve-year-old boy?'

'You are to do nothing, DCI Whitworth.'

'But...'

'You are to continue with your surveillance but do nothing to jeopardise this operation, is that clear?'

Charlie didn't answer, his eyes frantically moving left and right searching for a solution.

'I said you are to do nothing except carry on with your surveillance.'

Ridpath stared at Charlie. The surveillance detective shrugged his shoulders. A sound clicked and the tape on the recorders began to revolve. Muffled voices came through the speakers.

'You just sit yourself down on the couch. What would you like to drink? A coke or something stronger?' Graham Connelly's Manchester whine.

A young boy's voice answered. 'Do you have a beer, Mr Connelly? I'd like a beer.'

'Coming right up. You should check out the video games and see which one you want to play.'

Charlie tried once more. 'But ma'am, I believe an offence is about to be committed...'

Claire Trent's voice cut him off. 'You have your orders, DCI Whitworth. Do you understand?'

'Yes, ma'am.'

Charlie clicked off the Airwave.

At the same time a male voice, Graham Connelly's, came through the speaker. 'Here's your beer, I hope San Miguel is ok; don't want you getting too drunk.' A rustling sound. 'You've chosen Assassin's Creed. It's great, I'm up to level 6 already. You put it in. I'm just going to get changed, get out of my street clothes. You want to get changed?'

The sound of XBox. 'Nah, it's ok.'

'Charlie you *have* to do something.' said Ridpath.

'What? You heard Trent. She gave me a direct order.'

Ridpath pointed out the window, 'There's a twelve-year-old kid over there, on his own with a known sex offender and you're going to do nothing?'

'You heard her. She gave me a direct order, I can do nothing.'

'But…'

'But she didn't give you a direct order, Ridpath. She doesn't even know you're here.' He turned to the surveillance officer. 'Grant, was DI Ridpath with me tonight?'

'Who? Never heard of him, boss.'

Ridpath stood up. 'I'll just go out to get some sandwiches and coffee.'

'There's a cafe round the corner that's open. I think they have a payphone too, just in case you want to call somebody.'

More voices through the speakers. 'Right, it's one on one. Before we start, you want another beer.'

'Ta, Mr Connelly, that would be great.'

'Did you hear, Grant?' Charlie leant forward cupping his left ear. 'Is that a domestic disturbance in the flat?'

'I'm not sure, Charlie, could be?'

Ridpath nodded once to Charlie and opened the door to the flat. As he was about to leave, his DCI said, 'after you've eaten, Ridpath, you don't need to come back. I'll handle everything from now on.'

Ridpath closed the door behind him.

Sometimes he hated his job.

This was one of those times.

# Chapter Forty-Two

As soon as Ridpath arrived home he headed straight for the shower, standing under it for fifteen minutes as the hot water rained down on his head.

What had just happened?

Had he really just gone against Claire Trent's direct order and rung in a false report to 999? The conversation kept flashing through his brain.

'Emergency, which service do you require?'

'Police.'

'What's the nature of the emergency?'

'It's my next door neighbour. He's hitting his wife. I can hear it. He's just shouted he's going to kill her.'

The woman on dispatch was calm and controlled. 'What's the address of the disturbance, sir.'

'Twenty-five Reston Street, flat 3B.'

'And your name, sir?'

'You've got to come quickly, I can hear them fighting.'

'A police car has already been dispatched. What is your name, sir?'

He put down the phone, his hand shaking as he did it.

Already, he could hear the distant whine of a police siren, getting closer. They were quick today.

He thought about going back to the surveillance post but Charlie had been clear. Let him handle it. So Ridpath had flagged down a cab and come straight home.

The water was going cold. He switched off the tap and stepped out into the bathroom, standing in front of the mirror.

Who was he now?

A man who, for the first time in his life, had disobeyed a direct order. OK, it wasn't given to him but he had heard it loud and clear. And yet he didn't feel guilty about what he did. Instead, a vague unhappiness, a disquiet, inhabited his body.

Was this why he had become a copper? To let paedophiles molest young children because preventing them would jeopardise an operation? Hadn't it been drilled into them time and time again their job was to serve the public not simply look for the next arrest or the next promotion?

What had happened?

He coughed twice. A harsh, wracking cough.

Better get dressed before I catch cold. That's the last thing I need.

He put on his clothes, all the time a sense of weariness hanging over him like a shroud. Was this why he had become a copper?

That night he drank far too much Laphroaig, emptying the bottle.

But he still slept badly.

# Day Five

*Sunday, April 22, 2018*

## Chapter Forty-Three

He woke up on Sunday morning with a slight hangover. Nothing too bad; just a dry, sticky mouth with the aftertaste of scotch coating his tongue.

After three mugs of strong coffee he rang Polly, hoping that Eve would be free and they could spend some time together.

All he reached was her voicemail. 'Polly Lim is busy at the moment as is her daughter. If you leave your name and number, we'll get back to you as soon as we can. If you are trying to sell me insurance or any other useless consumer item I don't need, you can bugger off. Bye...'

Ridpath tried again, this time leaving a message, hoping when she heard his voice she would pick up the phone.

But she didn't. Instead, the only thing he remembered was that she was calling herself Polly Lim now, her maiden name. She was no longer Polly Ridpath.

Not good.

Not good at all.

He switched on the local news. United had beaten Spurs 2-1 in the semi-final of the FA Cup, so the lads were off to Wembley. Should he try to get tickets, perhaps take Eve and Polly down to London for the weekend? He'd ask Polly when he saw her.

The rest of the news was the same old stuff. Verne Troyer had died. A woman had been assaulted on a late night bus. A punk festival was in town. The usual shenanigans on *Coronation Street*. Three people had been assaulted in Manchester city centre after a night on the town.

But nothing about the murder or any gang activity. GMP must have been pulling out all the stops to keep it quiet, but anybody with a pair of eyes would have noticed more police on the streets.

Perhaps he should go to police HQ? He was sure they needed some help. After three days on high alert, without any leave, there were bound to be some detectives who had called in sick.

But then he would have to spend time with Claire Trent and he didn't really want to face her, not after last night. Too many awkward questions.

Then he remembered City were playing at home today against Swansea so the jams on Oldham Road near HQ would be horrendous. Definitely another reason to avoid going anywhere near there.

He couldn't stay at home though, staring at four walls and an unopened bottle of Laphroaig staring at him.

So he decided to go into the office and clear up the rest of the backlog of work waiting for him. At least, he could start the week well.

He drove over to Stockfield, this time avoiding the M60, parking the car next to a disused church rather than paying extortionate rates for the car park.

He presumed the office would be empty, it was Sunday after all, but he found Margaret Challinor behind her desk.

'Morning, Ridpath. Didn't expect to see you here today.'

She was wearing a mauve wool jumper and jeans, with her grey hair pulled back into a ponytail, revealing the clearest skin and the absence of any wrinkles. It made her look young and youthful, belying her age.

'I thought I would clear the backlog of work.'

'Very commendable of you.'

'And you?'

'Same, really. Plus since my son and daughter have gone to university, I find the house a little quiet on a Sunday.'

'No husband?' Ridpath wondered whether he had over-stepped the mark and offended her in asking such a personal question.

Instead, she just laughed. 'He left long ago, for a younger model I'm afraid, and he's married again. Not to the woman he left me for though, somebody else. Doing rather well is John, a barrister, specialising in maritime law. And you, how are Polly and Eve?'

'They're fine.'

'Are you two still living apart?'

Ridpath nodded.

'Give her time. She just needs time.' Margaret Challinor smiled and then, as if embarrassed by their intimacy, immediately changed the subject. 'How was your meeting with Michael Connelly?'

'Not good.' Ridpath told her everything. 'You'll have to assign somebody else. I don't think he'll want to see somebody he knows is a copper.'

She shook her head. 'You're wrong. He rang my mobile this morning. He wants you to continue liaising with his family. He calls you that "bloody copper".'

Ridpath frowned. 'How did he get your mobile number?'

'I thought you had given it to him.'

'Why would I do that? Is it unlisted?'

'I don't think so.'

Ridpath frowned again. 'Be careful, Mrs Challinor. The Connellys are dangerous people, not to be trifled with.'

'I have no intention of "trifling" with anybody, Ridpath. He called me and I answered the phone. That's all.'

'Just be careful, Mrs Challinor.'

He turned to leave, but her voice called him back.

'Ridpath, the pathologist's report on Ronald Wilson has finally come in. I haven't read it yet but I think Jenny gave it to you. Can you look at it and tell me what you think?'

Was this a test or her trying to show she had confidence in him? Margaret Challinor had a degree in forensic science, she would be able to understand the report far better than him.

No matter.

'I'll get right on it and give you the topline.'

# Chapter Forty-Four

The brown envelope was sitting in the middle of his desk, no stamp or address.

Inside was a handwritten note.

> *For DI Ridpath,*
>
> *Here is a copy of my post-mortem report on the death of Ronald Wilson. I have sent copies to the Police and the Crown Prosecution Service. In my considered opinion the death was unnatural.*
>
> *If you would like to discuss any element of this report, please do not hesitate to contact me.*
>
> *I remain your obedient servant,*
> *James Schofield*

Ridpath turned over the nine-page report. It was in a new template he had not seen before and seemed to be detailed in the extreme. A quick glance revealed it was written in an opaque medical language. Luckily, Dr Schofield had also attached a shorter topline.

STATEMENT of WITNESS
Statement of: Dr James Schofield, BSc, MB, BS, MRC Path, DipRCPath (Forensic)
Age of Witness: 32
Occupation: Greater Manchester Police Pathologist
Address: Forensic Pathology Services

This statement consisting of 9 pages signed by me, is true to the best of my knowledge and belief and I make it knowing that, if tendered in evidence, I shall be liable to prosecution if I have wilfully stated in it anything I know to be false or do not believe to be true.

The bottom was signed and dated by Dr Schofield. Ridpath was amazed the man was thirty-two, but looked eighteen. But given his medical condition, it was to be expected.

He turned the page and continued to read.

FINAL POST-MORTEM REPORT

Mr Ronald Arthur Wilson – date of birth: 02.02.95.

At approximately 14:00 on April 12, at the request of Greater Manchester Police, I attended the scene of a suspicious death at Wingate Lake.

I was logged into the inner cordon of the scene at 14:05.

On arrival I was met by Detective Sergeant Harper and SOCO Albert Simpson.

At this point, I was given brief background information that the deceased appeared to be a Ronald Wilson who had been reported missing eleven days previously.

At approximately 13:05 the body had been discovered in the water by children playing in the park. Paramedics attended but due to the body being in the water were unable to declare that life was extinct.

Fact of death
After I met with the senior investigating officer and the lead SOCO, the body was removed from the

water and placed on the ground beside the lake. I then proceeded to examine the body itself for the purposes of verifying the fact of death.

This was confirmed at 15:27.

The body was of a young Caucasian male appearing to be of the stated age. The body was nearly naked, dressed only in a pair of blue boxer shorts. No clothes were found at the scene However, a witness reported a man entering the water previous to the discovery of the body. There were signs of prolonged immersion: wrinkling the skin of the soles and palms, with some loosening of the skin, hair and nails. Maceration of the skin seemed to be well established but (*vide* Polson and Gee 1973) detachment of the skin had not yet occurred, suggesting a time in the water of at least a week but less than two.

There was a visible brown birthmark on the right side of the neck.

A small injury was noted on the back of the head.

All the relevant tapings and swabs were taken.

An examination was made of the surrounding area but nothing further was discovered which related to our body. The police have issued a request to the general public that the clothes and wallet of the deceased should be returned but nobody has come forward so far.

Signs of visible injury
There were bite marks to the ear, shoulders, legs and toes that appear to have come from fish. One larger bite mark to the stomach may have been from a pike or similar carnivorous piscean. The SIO informed me the lake does contain several pike.

There was an injury to the rear of the skull.

The skin around the wrists showed evidence of trauma.

There were no other visible signs of injury to the body.

I was logged out of the scene at 17:12 and the body transported to the mortuary for a post-mortem, ordered by the coroner, Margaret Challinor.

## Protective clothing

During the course of the entire time I spent at the scene I wore protective overshoes, a hooded white scene suit, a pair of gloves and a mask. My personal dictaphone was enclosed in a protective evidence bag during the course of the examinations.

I was logged out of the cordon at 17:30.

The injuries were interesting, but everything else seemed standard for a body found in the water. Ridpath was surprised at the detail in the pathologist's report for a death the police thought was an accident or a possible suicide. Dr Schofield was conscientious, perhaps a consequence of being new? He turned over to the next page.

## POST-MORTEM EXAMINATION

On the morning of April 16, I attended the mortuary of Stepping Hill Hospital to undertake a specialist post-mortem on the body of Ronald Wilson.

The post-mortem commenced at 09:30 hours.

The people present were

A Simpson...SOC Manager
Kate Brady...Mortuary Technician

Photographs were taken under my direction and I performed the post-mortem examination. Received in a white, signature-sealed bodybag and wrapped in a black plastic sheet was the body I recognised from the scene. Head and hand bags were in place.

External examination
He was of medium build, weighed 74.2 kg and was 178 cm tall. His hair was sandy coloured and cut short to the head. The body was soiled from being immersed in water but not excessively so. As mentioned previously, maceration of the skin had occurred but not to any great degree.

An outer examination of the body revealed signs of a sharp force injury to the rear of the head at the left parietal scalp approximately 4 cm above and 2 cm behind the right ear. On removal of the scalp to the level of the nape of the neck posteriorly, this thin wound was seen to penetrate the skull and enter the brain to the depth of 2 inches. The wound was no more than 7mm round, suggesting it was the result of a sharp point (such as an awl or a thin ice pick) being driven into the skull with great force.

There is no likelihood this could have happened by accident as the body hit the water, i.e. by a reed or sharp piece of wood. There was no organic residue in any part of the wound. Reddening around the area of the wound indicated it happened ante-mortem.

The hands had a series of three minor incisions running in parallel on the inner aspect of the junction of the right wrist crease with the left hypothenar eminence (bulge of tissue at the base of the little finger). These were approximately 1.8 cm in length and are indicative of defensive injuries.

Both wrists showed abrasion marks and bruising suggesting the victim's wrists had at one point been tied but there was no evidence of rope discovered at the scene and the hands were free in the water when the body was found.

## Internal examination
### Evidence of drowning
The lungs and body were examined for evidence of freshwater drowning i.e. 'the process of experiencing respiratory impairment from submersion in a liquid'.

There was no evidence of active respiration of fresh water causing alveolar collapse/atelectasis, due to the alteration of the surface tension properties of pulmonary surfactant.

There was no evidence of electrolyte dilution and hypervolaemia due to fresh water being absorbed into the bloodstream.

There was no evidence of myocardial depression, reflex pulmonary vasoconstriction or altered pulmonary capillary permeability contributing to pulmonary oedema from systemic hypoxaemia.

And the classic findings ascribed to drowning i.e. external foam visible at the mouth or nostrils, frothy fluid in the airways and lung 'hyper-expansion' were not present (although none of these is diagnostic).

### Toxicology
The length of time spent in the water prevents a conclusive study of the toxicology of the victim. However:

Trace elements of Ambien were found.

No alcohol present (usually a contributing factor to any drowning)

No other drugs were found in the system.

Attached is the Toxicology Report. Appendix
1

Heart

Normal for a twenty-one-year-old man. Slicing the myocardium showed no pallor in the Fossa Ovalis. Ventricular dimensions were in normal parameters as were the pericardium, atna, major blood vessels and the valves.

Attached is a list of the organ weights. Appendix 2

Ridpath was a little lost given all the technical language. He turned the page and breathed a sigh of relief.

CONCLUSIONS

1. There are three major reasons for finding a body in the water: accident, suicide or the disposal of a body that has been murdered elsewhere.

2. Accidental death would reveal the presence of water in the lungs and other determinants of death by drowning. None were found.

3. And again, suicide by drowning would show the same determinants.

4. Examination of the skull reveals a deep wound to the back of the head caused by a sharp instrument.

5. Defensive wounds on the hands suggest this victim tried to protect himself during an attack.

6. The wrists were bound at one point before the man died.

I would conclude this is not a suicide or an accidental drowning, but the disposal of a body that had been killed prior to entering the water.

Therefore I give as cause of death:

Category 3. Murder by person or persons unknown.

Signed James Schofield, Pathologist. 19 April 2018

Ridpath read through the full report again, making sure he understood everything.

It looked like the pathologist was saying the death of Ronald Wilson wasn't an accident or suicide but murder.

Inside the file was a separate envelope containing photographs of the crime scene and those taken at the postmortem.

He hesitated for a moment before opening the envelope. Looking at dead bodies and close-ups of human livers was not something he enjoyed. It reminded him far too much of his own brush with mortality. There but for the grace of God and the care of the miracle workers at Christies, it could have been him on that cold, steel mortuary table.

Gingerly, he took out the sheaf of photographs, staring at the one on top of the pile.

His mouth dropped open. 'That can't be,' he said out loud, 'it's impossible.'

# Chapter Forty-Five

'All this new policing malarkey, it does me head in. What the fuck does "hot desking" mean anyway, Charlie? And yesterday I got a memo entitled "Operational Paradigms in Contemporary Fiduciary Exigencies" from some tosser on the sixth floor. Jesus. I didn't know what the hell he was talking about and I hadn't even started reading it.'

Dave Hardy stubbed his cigarette out in the overflowing ashtray on the car's dashboard. 'It's all these bloody courses they go on, isn't it? Fills their heads up with so much rubbish, they have to put it down on paper.'

They were sitting in an unmarked car outside the taxi office on Halcombe Road. All pretence at covert surveillance had been abandoned now in favour of letting Connelly and his men know they were watching their every move.

On the back seat of the car an assortment of McDonald's fries boxes, filet-o-fish wrappers, a couple of empty buckets of KFC and four used Starbucks cups were tossed waiting to be collected and thrown when the next shift arrived. The usual nutrition for a stakeout; a diet of fags and fast food.

There had been a few people going in and out of the taxi hut but it had been reasonably quiet since their arrival that morning at six a.m. The bodyguards were still there though, rubbing their arms and stamping their feet against the cold of spring.

It was Charlie who broke the silence. 'I remember going on a course in London once, run by the National Crime Agency. Three days it was and the title said "The Future of Policing. The 21st century and beyond." Well, you know me, I was just

202

there for the Fullers and to see some old mates. United were playing Arsenal so I thought I could squeeze in a game too. After the pizza throwing incident at Old Trafford, I always liked us to take Wenger's mob to the cleaners. Didn't show no respect to Sir Alex.' Charlie stroked his moustache. 'I remember this tosser stood up in a room full of coppers and said two things. Number one was the forty-three regional police forces should be scrapped in favour of one national force...'

'I bet that went down like a cup of cold sick.'

'You're not kidding. You should have seen their faces. The room was full of superintendents and assistant commissioners, all of them just seeing their chances of any promotion vanish in one sentence. Then the mug, I think he was a super himself but one of the fast trackers, been to some university or other, anyway, he then dug his grave even deeper when he said the police force wasn't up to the job any more. The future is in criminal profiling, computer segmentation, airborne drones, proactive detention and big data, whatever that is.'

'Well, he wasn't wrong there. Years of cuts have seen to that.'

'What do you mean, Dave?'

'Well, look at this. How long do you thing we can keep this up?'

'The surveillance?' Charlie asked.

Dave nodded.

'About four more days, a week tops.'

'And after that?'

'We'll pull everybody off. Can't afford the costs.'

'And how many men are we using for this operation?'

'You know better, Dave, it's officers not men. Anyway the answer is more than seventy.'

'So Connelly, Big Terry and the rest know this. They are just waiting for us to go back into our shells and return to the comfort of our nicks before they decide to kick the war off. It will be like ninety-nine all over again, but this time they will be better armed. But...' he paused for a moment, 'what if there were drones just flying over Big Terry's pub and his house. Or observing the taxi shed. One man could monitor them all sat on his arse at the nick, watching a few screens. A couple of squad cars on call and Bob's your uncle.'

'Ah, but it doesn't have the human element, Dave. What happens if they all leave at once? A drone can't decide which one to follow.'

'Most of our plods can't either. But that's where technology comes in. What if everybody were fitted with a little chip in the gap between his finger and thumb. I saw it on telly last week. You can open doors with the chip, even pay for your coffee with it. Just put your skin next to the reader.'

'That'd be handy. Get it…' Charlie punched Dave Hardy on the arm.

The DS carried on anyway. 'You know you can track those chips like we track a mobile phone. All we do is sit down in front of our computers and look at the screen. We'd know where all the villains were and what they were doing.'

'So you mean instead of sitting here in a cold car eating shitty food, we could be sitting at home with a glass of Boddies in our hands looking at a screen and saying, "Burglar Bill is outside the house in Lymm again, should we nab him now or have another beer?".'

'That's it. But they probably won't let us drink on duty.'

Charlie pulled his moustache. 'There's one big problem with this Brave New World of yours, Dave.'

'What's that?'

'Who nabs Burglar Bill? In the end, some poor plod has to walk away from his screen and eventually arrest someone.'

'Robots.'

'Robots? *Terminator 2* and all that crap? I can just see it now. Yes sir, here we have the latest model. We've called it Dave Hardy. It's fat, drinks too much, farts like a trooper and can't run very fast, but it's a robot.'

'Don't be like that, Charlie. It's the future…'

'The future my arse. The future is going to be like the past for people like us. We investigate a crime, find evidence, build a case, arrest the perp and leave the rest to the mess that is the CPS and the criminal justice system. The life of a copper. Never has changed, won't ever change. End of story.'

Dave Hardy grabbed his arm. 'Looks like summat's up.'

One of Michael Connelly's thugs was walking towards their car. He tapped on the driver side window. Charlie pressed the button to lower it.

The bullet head with a broken nose spoke to them. 'Mr Connelly's sending me to Costa's. He wants to know if he can get you anything.'

Dave Hardy leant forward. 'Two lattes. Mine's with two sugars.'

'Any sugars for you, Mr Whitworth.'

Charlie shook his head

'Anything else while I'm there?'

'I could murder a bacon and egg roll,' said Dave Hardy.

'Is that it?'

Dave Hardy nodded.

'Ok, won't be long. And Mr Connelly says it's on the house. He doesn't reckon you'll be here much longer anyway.'

Charlie rolled the window up and looked at Dave Hardy.

'What? I was hungry.'

'I was just thinking you don't have to feed robots bacon and egg rolls.'

# Chapter Forty-Six

Ridpath flicked through the other photographs of Ronald Wilson lying dead on the slab in the mortuary.

He was staring into the dead eyes of the man with the gun on the M60.

But that can't be. The accident only happened on Wednesday and Ronald Wilson's body had been discovered six days before, on April 12. A dead man can't get up from a mortuary table and walk, can he?

He closed his eyes bringing up the memory of the man with the gun, and the moment when his hood blew off, revealing the face.

It was him.

It was definitely him.

Ridpath grabbed the report and rushed next door to see Margaret Challinor. She was in a meeting with the area coroner, Carol Oates. Both of them working on a Sunday, they must have been busy in his absence.

'Can it wait?'

'I'm afraid not.'

'Can you give us a moment, Carol?'

The young woman rolled her eyes, taking her files off the desk and left the room without looking at Ridpath.

'This better be important.'

He placed the report on her desk and watched her read it, her eyes scanning the page quickly and reaching the conclusions by Dr Schofield.

'It seems we have a murder on our hands, Ridpath. Have you told the police yet?'

'Not yet. I thought there were two things you should know first.'

'What?'

'The toxicology, the ropes around the wrists and the lack of clothes, just underwear, well, they are exactly the same as Gerard Connelly.'

'Our victim on the M60?'

Ridpath nodded,

'Shit.'

'That's what I said, Mrs Challinor.'

'So you think the two cases are linked?'

Ridpath nodded. 'But it's worse. Have you looked at the post-mortem pictures?'

'I tend to save that dubious pleasure for last.' She looked through the sheaf of photographs. 'The usual horror show, perhaps the lighting is a bit better than normal on these.'

'It's the first one that's important.'

She picked up the face and chest picture of Ronald Wilson lying on the mortuary table and stared at it. 'This is our victim?'

Ridpath nodded again. 'And he is also the man I saw with the gun on the M60 chasing after Gerard Connelly.'

The coroner snorted. 'Impossible.' She quickly flicked back through the report checking the dates. 'This man died at least two weeks before the accident...'

Ridpath sat down in Carol Oates' chair. 'I know it's impossible, but I swear it's the same man.'

Margaret Challinor stared at him for a long while.

'There's nothing wrong with me, you know. I'm not hallucinating or imagining things.'

The coroner shook her head. 'You are sure this is the same man, Ridpath?' She tapped the picture once with an elegantly manicured nail.

Ridpath nodded. 'I'd stake my life on it.'

'You may have to.' She played with the string of pearls around her neck. 'If what you say is true, what are you going to do about it?'

Ridpath ran his fingers through his hair. 'I hadn't thought.'

'Well, you'd better start. The postponed inquest on Ronald Wilson reopens on Thursday. I really don't want to postpone it again. The body should be released back to the family.'

Ridpath thought of the man's grandmother waiting to talk with an undertaker about the funeral. 'But you can't release the body while the police are investigating.'

'I know.' She stared at the post-mortem report. 'But it seems your discovery means the two cases are linked. The death of Gerard Connelly and this man.' The elegant nail tapped the photograph.

Once again, Margaret Challinor had cut right to the heart of the matter. His brain was trying to process the ramifications of what she had said. Logically, it wasn't possible this man and the man he had seen with the gun were one on the same. And he didn't believe in bloody ghosts. There must be an answer. The truth must be out there somewhere.

Margaret Challinor was still speaking. He caught the end of the sentence.

'...what are you going to do?'

'First, I need to talk to the pathologist and confirm his findings.'

The coroner nodded. 'Good idea. Check the photos too. Always look for Mr Cock-up. Has some tired technician put the wrong photographs in the file?'

'It happens,' Ridpath agreed.

'After that?'

Ridpath thought for a moment. 'I don't think we know enough about the family. If the two cases are linked, then I need to talk with Mrs Granger again.'

'OK, but when are you going to tell the police? If it's a murder, they need to investigate again. And if the two cases are linked Claire Trent needs to know.'

Ridpath wasn't looking forward to the conversation. 'Not yet. Let me get the facts straight first. She's got a lot on her plate, the last thing she needs right now is to go chasing after a false alarm.'

The coroner stared at him. 'Not like you to be so cautious, Ridpath.'

'Once bitten, twice shy. And in my case, you can teach an old dog new tricks. I'll tell her at the briefing tomorrow. Today is about getting the facts straight.'

'Two cliches in one sentence, Chief Superintendent Trent will be pleased.'

The face of his boss flashed through his mind. 'If I told her about a dead man killing Gerard Connelly, she'd lock me away and chuck the key in the Mersey.'

'But we can't wait forever. You have till Thursday, Ridpath, to solve this. That's when I have to reopen the inquest on Ronald Wilson.'

'It's not a lot of time, Mrs Challinor.'

'You'd better get moving then.' She put her black-rimmed glasses back on and began to open a file. 'Can you send Carol back in?'

He was being dismissed. He stood up and walked towards the door, stopping just as he touched the old brass handle.

'I'm not imagining it, Mrs Challinor.'

She looked up from her reading. 'I'm sure you're not, Ridpath. Nobody would invent such a story. And besides, I trust your judgement and your memory. If you tell me the men are the same, I believe you.'

'Thank you.'

'But remember, thousands won't. You need proof and you need evidence.'

'You sound like Charlie Whitworth.'

She smiled. 'Perhaps, myself and Chief Inspector Whitworth can finally agree about something.'

'You're right, but there's one thing I need above all.'
'What's that, Ridpath?'
'I need the truth.'

# Chapter Forty-Seven

'Big Terry will be going apeshit. His beloved son wasted with his dick cut off.' She threw the *Manchester Evening News* down on the table. 'That was a lovely idea of yours.'

'We learnt it out in Afghanistan from the Mujahideen. They first started using it in the 1980s. Put the fear of God in the minds of the young Russian conscripts. By the end, they had it down to an art form.'

'You all set for tonight?'

'As I always am.'

'Wear something dark and a hat. No need to wake the neighbours.'

'Mr Invisible, that's me...'

'...we'll go in and do it quick, understand?'

He threw her a loose salute. 'You're worse than my CO.'

'No, I'm far better than your CO. I'm still alive, remember?'

His CO had died along with five other officers in a helicopter strike in Helmand. Some Taliban had taken a lucky shot with an RPG. Seconds later the helicopter was lying on the valley floor, a heap of smoking, twisted metal, the stench of gasoline and human flesh heavy in the air.

He'd got out soon afterwards, there was no point being in the army any more.

What should he die for? Just so some politician could boast they had made the Western world safer for democracy?

What a load of bollocks. Tell that to all the widows of the men who died in the parched, rock-strewn cesspit they call a country.

He had gone north soon after arriving back in the UK. Gone back to Manchester to follow up on the story his mother had whispered to him on her death bed, the cancer eating up her breasts and her soul.

'He killed your father. Pretended to be his friend but that bastard killed your father.'

At first, she didn't believe him, the sister now sitting opposite him in the kitchen. The sister he never knew existed until his mother told him the truth. But the clues, and the lies, began to pile up until she could reach no other conclusion.

He had killed their father.

After that, it was only a matter of time before she worked out a plan. He quickly learned she was as clever as she was ruthless. Nothing could get in their way. Not even their own brother.

Her voice brought him back to the present.

'You're sure you can take care of it?'

'No worries.'

'It must be silent. No screams, no fighting.'

'What are we going to do with the body?'

'We leave it where it is.'

'Won't it be discovered?'

'Of course, but not until later and by then it will be far too late. One last thing; don't forget the gloves. We must leave no trace behind. Nothing easy for the police to work on.'

She stood up and headed for the stairs. 'I'm going for a nap,' she shouted over her shoulder.

His sister was the coolest woman ever. Only she could sleep before they were going to commit a murder.

## Chapter Forty-Eight

He parked the car on the double yellow lines outside the pathologist's apartment on Duke's Place close to the old Roman fort of Mamucium. The partial remains of a granary and the western wall jutted two feet out of a grass lawn. A vague memory came back to him from his time at university. One historian had called these bits of stone 'the least interesting Roman remains in Britain.'

Looking at them, he could see why. For a start, they weren't even real. A metal sign proudly stated they were a 'reconstruction' created because the Industrial Revolution had destroyed most of the original remains. That was Manchester, always sacrificing the past in the chase for something new.

In front of him a modern yellow tram clanked across a raised viaduct, rattling the Victorian pillars. He turned to face the pathologist's apartment. It was depressingly ugly in the modern utilitarian city centre style; all red brick, grey paint and tiny balconies serving no purpose except to provide storage space for a few tired plants and upright bikes.

He had called the pathologist after his meeting with Margaret Challinor. The man had informed him grumpily it was his day off and he was going to do nothing except sleep and then go to a film at HOME, some art house Polish thing Ridpath had never heard of.

At first, he had been reluctant to allow Ridpath to come to his home but after pleading his case, the detective was finally granted ten minutes, but no longer 'as a special favour'.

Ridpath pressed the intercom and it was immediately answered as if the man was hovering over the screen in his flat. 'Come up,' said the curt voice followed by the click of the door.

The lobby of the building was as charmless as the outside, with not one ounce of character save for a tired bunch of flowers next to the lift. Ridpath touched them. They were plastic.

The front door opened as soon as Ridpath exited on the fourth floor.

'Come in, you have ten minutes. I normally never allow people into my home. I'm making a special exception for you, Ridpath. I've been working all night, somebody decided to jump in the canal near the Gay Village after a row with his boyfriend.'

'Not the best thing to do.'

'I agree. They fished his body out at four o'clock this morning. So please make this as quick as you can.' The last sentence was said as the man walked down a short corridor to the living room.

Ridpath followed him. The area was not large, but spotlessly clean, almost obsessively so. Magazines were stacked neatly on a black coffee table. The walls were a stark white with one single picture; a vague blue–green abstract looking like it had been picked up from Ikea. The furniture was grey, modern and uncomfortable. Probably from Ikea as well.

'I won't offer you coffee, you won't be staying long enough to drink it.'

In the stark comfort of his home and out of his uniform of a white coat, the pathologist looked even younger. A grey T-shirt and sweat pants making him look like a teenager at some unfashionable party.

Ridpath ignored the lack of coffee and sat down at the pine table. Another import from the far north no doubt.

'Thank you for agreeing to see me, Dr Schofield.' He opened the file which contained the post-mortem report on Ronald Wilson. 'Sorry, I only just saw this today.'

'You work on a Sunday, Ridpath. I didn't think the coroner was so busy.'

Ridpath ignored the jibe. 'In this report, you make it clear you believe the death of Ronald Wilson was murder not an accident or suicide. Is that correct?'

'Read my report. I thought that I made myself clear?'

It was like dealing with a stroppy teenager. 'You did, Dr Schofield, I just want you to make it clear for me and for the coroner.'

The pathologist sighed and pulled out a chair to sit down next to Ridpath. 'What do you want to know?'

'How can you be so certain?'

'Deaths by fresh water drowning have three clear signs. Funnily enough, they were first noted in thirteenth century China by a man called Sung Tz'u. They are the presence of water in the lungs, removal of the surfactants covering the alveoli, cerebral oedemas or mastoid haemorrhages. Ronald Wilson displayed none of these signs ergo he was already dead when he entered the water. When these are combined with the wound on the back of the head...'

'Caused by a sharp instrument, you said.'

'An awl, auger or trepan. Even a knitting needle would serve the purpose. Add in defence wounds to the hands and my conclusion is this man was attacked and murdered before his body was placed in Wingate Lake.'

Ridpath pulled the photograph from the envelope. 'Is this the man you performed the post-mortem on?'

The doctor glanced at the photograph. 'Of course, it is. The photograph is in the post-mortem folder.'

'It's important you look at it closely, doctor.'

James Schofield sighed but picked up the photograph anyway, staring at it and comparing the numbers on it with those at the top of his report. 'This is Ronald Wilson. See I noted the birthmark on his neck in my report.' The doctor pointed to a small brown discolouration on the victim's neck and to the line on the report.

'So you are absolutely certain this is Ronald Wilson's picture.'

A heavy roll of the eyes. 'That's what I just said. Why are you wasting my time, Ridpath?'

'Because this is the man I saw with the gun standing at the side of the M60.

# Chapter Forty-Nine

Schofield snorted. 'Impossible, Ronald Wilson had been dead for between seven and ten days when I examined him beside the lake. You must be mistaken.'

'I know what I saw, Dr Schofield.'

The pathologist smiled pityingly. 'The science doesn't lie, Ridpath. It might not tell the truth all the time, but it doesn't lie.'

Ridpath realised he was facing the same problem again. Why didn't people believe him? The presence of the man with the gun in the first place and now this. Was it something to do with his face? He would try once more. He pulled out a copy of the E-Fit composite created last Wednesday night.

'Look, they are virtually identical.'

Dr Schofield examined the post-mortem picture and the E-Fit. 'They're close, I'll give you that. But many young men in Manchester look similar. These composite pictures are notoriously unreliable.' The pathologist glanced at his watch.

'Just one more thing, if I can bother you.'

'Go ahead, I still have time before my film. And this visit hasn't been as boring as I expected.'

Ridpath opened the pathologist's report on Ronald Wilson. 'You mentioned in your report about marks on the arms. Could you explain them further?'

'It was a difficult post-mortem. The body had been in the water for quite a time. The skin deteriorates and begins to slough off. You'll understand it becomes more and more difficult to determine the extent and nature of superficial bruising or scarring.'

'I understand, but...'

'But I was able to see marks looking like rope burns or scars around the wrists.'

'Were the hands tied when the body was placed in the water?'

'I don't think so. There were no ropes around the wrists when the body was found.'

'But you think the wrists may have been bound before then?'

'That's what I said, DI Ridpath. Why are you asking me about this?'

'Well, it's just Gerard Connelly also displayed rope marks around his wrists. And he was found just wearing boxer shorts.'

'So?'

'But there's more. Both had traces of Ambien in their systems according to toxicology.'

'I see where you are going. You think the two deaths may be linked?'

'Exactly. Is there anything we could do scientifically or forensically to compare the marks or the Ambien?'

The pathologist thought for a moment, his hand stroking his hairless chin. 'Ambien is a sleeping tablet. It's not commonly prescribed any more in the UK. It's used far more often in America. No real way of comparing the two results using toxicology I'm afraid. The body breaks down the drug pretty quickly.'

'What about the rope marks on the wrists?'

'We could compare the skin visually under a microscope. It's not done normally. We could even take it further, comparing a sample of the skin beneath an electron scanning microscope. The body was in the water but minute fragments of rope may still be attached. The problem is time and money...'

'If I could get the coroner to order you to perform the tests, could you do it?'

'It may not reveal anything, the body...'

'I know, was in the water for a long time.'

The pathologist stood up. 'Let me see what I can do when I get back to work tomorrow. I'll also compare the upper torso scarring between the two victims.

Ridpath stood up and held out his hand. 'Thanks for your time, doctor.'

'Actually, thank you, Ridpath. It's an interesting problem, I may even be able to get a paper out of this. Science is very competitive these days, important to get peer reviews.'

For a man who looked like a teenager, the doctor had a competitive streak inside him. Ridpath didn't care, as long as it helped him solve this bloody case.

Ridpath walked towards the door. As he did, he heard the pathologist call his name and he turned back.

The doctor was still staring at the E-Fit picture. 'Just an idea. Looking at this picture, they could be brothers? Have you thought about that?'

# Chapter Fifty

Ridpath sat outside in his car going over the meeting he had just had with the pathologist. A brother. Of course, why didn't he think of it? If Ronald Wilson had a brother it would certainly solve the problem of the timeline. It might also give a motive for the murder of Gerard Connelly.

Had Ronald been killed by the Connellys and that's why a brother would seek revenge?

But why had Mrs Granger said nothing about other children? He checked Tommy Harper's police report once more.

Nothing. He had to go and visit her. Ask her all the questions Tommy Harper should have asked in the initial police investigation.

Ridpath glanced across at the ancient Roman ruins, built thirty years ago by Manchester Corporation. The Romans handled their criminals with a shocking ruthlessness; just fed them to the lions or forced them to fight as gladiators. It might be a solution to Manchester's gang problem: The Gladiator Games this Saturday at Old Trafford. The Connellys vs Big Terry and his mob. Come one, come all. Family seating available. Tickets available at your local nick.

He shook his head. He really was losing it. Pull yourself together Ridpath. And then he realised he hadn't had a cigarette all day. Even better, he didn't even want one. What's more, he was enjoying the job. At last, this felt like real detective work; putting together all the varied bits of evidence to work out what had actually happened. He knew he wasn't there yet, but he was getting closer, he could feel it in his water. Perhaps this coroner's job was going to work out after all. At least, it felt like a step in the right direction.

He called Mrs Granger's number on his mobile. It rang and rang and rang without an answer machine kicking in. Where was she? She was hardly the most mobile person in the world. Had the next door neighbour taken her out shopping? She said it usually happened on Friday Maybe she'd been busy and decided to take her today instead.

He rang again. Still no answer. He was about to put his car in gear to drive over to her address when his phone rang.

'Hello, Mrs Granger, I'm glad you phoned back...'

'Ridpath, I didn't know you were seeing other women.'

It was Polly's voice. 'I'm not... I'm just... it's...' he stuttered.

'I know, I was just teasing you. I was wondering if... I mean, Eve was wondering if you are free this afternoon. There's another film on in Didsbury she wants to see and she asked me if you wanted to come too.'

Ridpath was about to answer that he was busy and had to work when he remembered what he had promised himself. 'No, I've just finished what I'm doing. What time is the film?'

'It's *Wonder Woman* at five o'clock.'

'I thought she'd seen it already.'

'She has, but she likes the idea of women kicking arse, so she wants to see it again. If you don't want to go, that's ok, I'll take her.'

Ridpath glanced at his watch, 3:30 p.m.. He would maybe call Mrs Granger after the film, she was bound to be back by then. 'I'm in town about half an hour away. I'll pick you both up from the Chinese Dragon's house at 4:15 this afternoon.'

'You mean my mother?'

'Her as well. She's not coming is she?' Ridpath asked crossing his fingers.

'She's got a mah-jong session with her pals. They've been "swimming" since this morning. Me and Eve have to get out of the bloody house. The shouts of "Pong" are starting to drive us both crazy.'

'Ok, see you soon.'

He clicked off the phone. He would definitely call Mrs Granger after the film. Perhaps he could go round tomorrow morning before the meeting at police HQ.

The old woman wasn't going too far, not at her age.

## Chapter Fifty-One

Elsie Granger edged her Zimmer frame 3 inches forward, shuf-fling her feet, one arm resting on the Zimmer frame and the other holding a mug of tea.

Slowly, deliberately, without spilling a drop, she set the tea down on the dresser next to her chair.

'Such a palaver over making a cuppa,' she said out loud, glancing across at the television. Now she just had time to go back for her piece of salmon in lemon sauce before the evening news began. She liked watching the news, it always reminded her there were some people worse off in this world.

She rotated the Zimmer frame around an inch at a time. It wouldn't do to fall at her age. Look at Mr Gillespie at number sixty-seven. He'd been on his living room floor for six hours before somebody found him. All that time lying there with a broken hip. The pain must have been terrible. It couldn't happen to her, not with living alone now, with Ronnie being gone.

She inched the Zimmer frame forward with her forearms on the padded rests. Her knees were painful this evening, perhaps it was going to rain tomorrow. That was the problem with living in Manchester, it was always going to rain tomorrow.

'Careful now, Elsie, watch the carpet rod at the door, can't have you tripping up over it.' She often talked out loud to herself these days, more to hear the sound of a human voice than anything else.

A voice. Any voice.

Some weeks she went for days without seeing or hearing anybody except the men on the telly. The loneliness hurt her. It felt like a gaping hole inside her stomach that could never be filled. All through her life she had never been a terribly social person. It was enough having Fred and Ronald around. She didn't need anybody else. And then there was God too. Her Holy Trinity, she used to joke with the priest. A lovely man was Father Alphonsus.

But since he had moved on she didn't get along with the new, young one that had taken over the church. And now both Fred and Ronald had gone too.

She reached up to dip her fingers in the holy water beneath the picture of Christ on the wall in the hall, making the sign of the cross, before shuffling forward into the kitchen.

Even God had left her too. She never felt his presence any more. It was as if she were all alone in the world.

The phone rang in the living room. She'd never make it back in time before they rang off. It was only another man trying to sell her double-glazing anyway. Not many people rang her any more. Why would they?

She reached the microwave and pressed the button to open the door. Inside, the fish was steaming in its bath of lemon sauce. She grasped the bowl in her arthritic fingers. It was funny, she didn't feel hot or cold any more. It was all the same to her. A reaction to all the drugs she took perhaps.

Holding the bowl in her right hand, she shifted the Zimmer frame along, just resting her left arm on the pad.

Funny, she had made this journey so many times in her life. Fetching and carrying for Fred and Ronald. She had been a good wife and mother. A damn sight better mother than her daughter, Doreen.

And now Fred and Ronnie were gone. She would follow soon. She hoped it would be soon.

The evening news was about to start when she heard the noise behind her.

'Who's there?' she shouted.

No answer.

Was it the cat from next door? He was always sitting on her kitchen window sill. Perhaps he was out on the prowl tonight after a few mice or his oats.

'Cats don't eat oats,' she said out loud, chuckling to herself.

She set the bowl down next to her tea and manoeuvred herself around so she was standing directly in front of her chair. She dropped down on it and sat there for a few seconds recovering her breath.

Another sound in the kitchen. This time she was sure it was something breaking. She tried to still her breath, sitting up in her chair to listen intently. Had she left a glass too close to the edge of the sink? Had it fallen? Or had the neighbour's cat knocked over a milk bottle?

Then she remembered there weren't any milk bottles any more. Nor any milkmen. How she missed the rattle of the milk float early in the morning on the cobblestones of the street.

Footsteps.

She was sure she heard footsteps.

They were going upstairs. Why would anybody want to go upstairs?

The door swung slowly open.

'Who's there?' she shouted, reaching for the knitting needle at her feet. 'Who's there?' Louder now. Holding the knitting needle in her arthritic hands like a knife ready to stab forward.

'It's just us, come to see you. We haven't seen each other for such a long time, Elsie.'

A blonde-haired woman stepped out of the dark of the hall into the glowing light from the television.

Mrs Elsie Granger noticed the glint of steel in the woman's hand.

It was the last thing she would ever notice.

# Day Six

*Monday, April 23, 2018*

# Chapter Fifty-Two

For the first time in a long while Detective Inspector Thomas Ridpath drove to work with a broad smile on his face.

Eve and Polly had spent the night at home. The family was back together again, even though it had only been for a few short hours. Eve had insisted they return home after the film so she could pick up a few things from her room. One thing led to another and she was insisting she had to spend the night with her 'boys' watching over her. The pictures of the Korean boy band BTS.

There had been a moment of embarrassed silence until he offered to spend the night on the couch. He knew Polly well. If he wanted the family to get back together again, it was going to be a long process of baby steps to show he had changed.

Inevitably, the conversation shifted towards his cancer.

'You've been keeping the check-up appointments?'

'Religiously.'

'And?'

'All clear last month, I went again on Friday to allow the vampire to take more blood and see Dr Morris. He seemed very happy with my progress. I'll get the results soon.'

'You've been looking after yourself?'

'I think so. Eating well, drinking less and I haven't smoked for the last two days.' The first two were little white lies but at least the latter was true.

'That's good, Ridpath. And the house is spotless too.'

Luckily, he had decided to give the place a clean yesterday, before then it had been a tip.

She opened the cupboards and the fridge in the kitchen. 'Not much food, though. Are you really eating well?'

'You know me, I hate cooking. Eating out more than I should but at least I'm eating.'

'You should always have food at home, it's much better for you.'

'I know. Listen Polly, I realise it's up to me to take more responsibility for my health and welfare. It's the least I can do for you and Eve.'

She'd just nodded and said she was going to bed. He'd given her a hug, hoping against hope she would ask him to join her, but she hadn't.

Never mind, baby steps.

The morning had been wonderfully chaotic. He had risen early to pour cornflakes for Eve and boil a couple of eggs for Polly, toasting a few rounds of stale-ish bread in case they were hungry.

As was normal, Eve came down and grumpily ate her cereal without speaking. Polly drank her coffee and put the eggs in her handbag for later, fretting all the time she was going to be late for school whilst he devoured the toast, watching all the frenetic activity of getting ready.

'Where's your schoolbag?' asked Polly.

'I dunno, where did you put it?' answered Eve pulling on her school socks.

'At your grandma's, that's where it is. Ridpath…'

'I'll drive you both there and then take you onto the school.'

'Eve, hurry, we're going to be late. The Wicked Witch of the West is going to kill me.'

'You shouldn't talk about the headmistress like that. Mrs Roberts is always very nice to me. Says I have lovely hand-writing'

'She would, wouldn't she? You're her star pupil. I, on the other hand, am known as the teacher who is always late.' Polly glanced at her watch. 'And if we don't get a move on, I'm going to be the late Polly Ridpath.'

228

It was a typical morning in the Ridpath household. How he had missed them. He also noticed she had called herself Polly Ridpath.

Baby steps.

He hustled them both out of the house into the car and drove them to the dragon's house, waiting outside while Eve and Polly both picked up their school things before dropping them off at their school.

As soon as they arrived Eve rushed off to see her friends, while Polly sat in the car.

'Thanks, Ridpath, I really enjoyed last night.'

'It was good to be a family again, wasn't it?'

She nodded, glancing at the car's clock. 'Is that the time? The Witch will kill me.' She leant over, gave him a peck on the cheek and was gone.

Now he was on his way to the briefing. Would he face a Claire Trent out for his blood because of the phone call? Or had Charlie handled it? And what would he do about his new information? Tell them about it or keep quiet until the pathologist rang him back?

He still hadn't contacted Mrs Granger. That would have to be his first job after the briefing. Without her information he would leave himself open to sneers and disbelief from both Charlie and Detective Superintendent Claire Trent. There were too many questions still requiring answers.

He parked in the open-air HQ car park and headed up to the briefing room. It was chucking it down with rain and of course he didn't have an umbrella in the car. How can you drive in Manchester without an umbrella? Then he remembered Polly had taken it, so he pulled his jacket tighter around his chest and dashed through the downpour to the main building.

The briefing room was already full by the time he arrived. A young DC made him sign the register and he found a place next to Harry Makepeace.

'Morning.'

'Is it? I've been up all night watching that bloody taxi shed and Michael Connelly. You know he sleeps there? Silly tosser.'

There was the sound of the banging of a fist on a table. The guvnor, Claire Trent, was standing at the front of the room with Chief Inspector Robinson. An unknown chief inspector in a uniform stood next to them both.

'Right, you lot, let's get started,' she bellowed.

The detectives gradually stopped talking and the few still standing rushed to find seats.

'We had a quiet weekend. And that's down to you lot watching over our targets and the extended police presence on the streets. Well done.'

'The quiet before the storm...' whispered Harry Makepeace beneath his breath.

Claire Trent continued. 'But we have to stay vigilant. Eventually there will be a retaliation from Big Terry's mob. My bet is they are just trying to work out who did it.'

'Same as us then...' Harry Makepeace whispered.

She pointed to a picture of the victim's body propped upright against the granite monument. Ridpath noticed the corpse was wearing a pair of blue boxer shorts exactly the same colour as Gerard Connelly.

'Dr Protheroe performed the post-mortem yesterday. He rang me with a topline report. Phil Marsland was shot from close range with a .38 calibre bullet. Death was probably instantaneous.'

'It sounds like an execution, ma'am.' It was Catherine Delaney speaking. She looked fresh and sprightly. Even from where Ridpath was sitting he could smell the scent of soap and a floral perfume.

'It probably was, Catherine, suggesting a pro hit. Do we have anything from intelligence, Robbo.'

The DCI shook his head. 'We haven't had any intelligence on killers for hire for a while. I'm afraid it's a resource issue. Most of our intelligence officers have been switched to counter-terrorism work.'

'What did Theresa May say about "crying wolf," Harry Makepeace whispered.

'The pathologist also confirmed the body hadn't been shot at the monument but elsewhere. He was probably moved there any time from noon to the minute he was found at 4:30, with a more likely placement time of two p.m. to four p.m. Doreen, how was the CCTV search for the vehicle that transported the body?'

The new female detective sergeant stood up. 'It's like looking for a needle in a haystack. Saturday is the busiest day for the Trafford Centre, ma'am. Roughly 25,000 vehicles an hour pass through the roundabout close to the church.'

'What about the bridge?'

'Barton Bridge is less busy, about 3,000 vehicles an hour cross it. So given our timings of noon to four p.m., that gives us approximately 12,000 cars to check through ANPR. Even then we're hoping for a link to a known associate of Michael Connelly. But what if it's one of the other gangs? And what if they didn't come from Eccles but down the M60. I'm afraid without tighter parameters it's like looking for a black cat in a dark room when you are blind.'

'Or a Man United fan looking for a goal?' said one detective.

'Nah, it's easier than that but still bloody near impossible.' She sat down again.

'Thanks Doreen. Keep going anyway, we may strike it lucky.'

'Anything from the area, Dave.'

Dave Hardy stood up and shook his head. 'There's nobody who lives in the area. The nearest houses are across the Manchester Ship Canal in Eccles. But nobody saw anything. I also checked up on the repair man who discovered the body. All his times and movements are accounted for.'

'Thanks, Dave. My interview with Big Terry was useless. All he told me was that his son was last seen going out at seven p.m. on Thursday night. Apparently he had some date with a woman that night. Big Terry didn't know who the woman was.

Phil Marsland didn't take his car but hired a taxi. We're checking which one as we speak.'

'Michael Connelly runs a taxi company,' said Charlie.

Claire Trent turned to the police support officer. 'Can you check his company too, Chrissy?'

'Will do, guvnor.'

'Anybody got anything from their CI's? Any word on the street?'

For half a second Ridpath was tempted to stick his hand up and reveal his latest information linking the murder of Graham Connelly to the death of Ronald Wilson, but he decided to wait. He had to get more information from both the pathologist and Mrs Granger. He wasn't going to make any half-cocked allegations without supporting evidence. The one concrete link he had was that both victims were wearing a pair of blue boxer shorts. But that wouldn't stand up in a court of law nor would it be accepted by Claire Trent.

A few detectives mentioned rumours of Michael Connelly's involvement, others suggested the Moss Side gang was involved, but there were no solid leads.

'Looks like we're stuck then. Protheroe's final report will come in later today, perhaps it will give us more. In the meantime I want you lot to shake the trees. Somebody must know something.' She pointed her finger at the room. 'I want a report from every one of you at the briefing tomorrow morning. *Every one of you*, no exceptions. Understand?'

There was a mumbled chorus of agreement.

'Now let's hear updates from those in charge of surveillance. Lorraine, you go first.'

The detective inspector stood up. 'As you say, guvnor, it was pretty quiet over the weekend with Big Terry. His mob all gathered in their usual pub, the Wheatsheaf. My bet is they were working out their next steps.'

'Did you get anybody in the pub?'

She shook her head. 'Only regulars allowed in. A few of the boys tried but they were turned away. The place is like a bloody fortress.'

'Thanks, Lorraine. Charlie, what about you?'

'We had a chat with Michael Connelly on Saturday. Of course, he denies any involvement in, or knowledge of, the murder of Phil Marsland. I think his son, Graham, may know more than he's letting on though. Separately, a car from the local nick went to his flat in the Northern Quarter on Saturday night in response to a report of domestic violence.'

'I thought Graham was gay?' said one of the detectives.

Charlie shrugged his shoulders. 'Anyway, they found nothing and went away.'

Ridpath was watching Claire Trent for her reaction. She had specifically ordered Charlie not to interfere in the behaviour of Graham Connelly. Would she rant and rave?

Nothing.

Just a simple nod of the head, followed by a question, 'Was our cover blown?'

'I don't think so. We watched him yesterday and there was no change in his routine. We even heard him ordering crack from his dealer.'

'We could nick him for possession,' said one of the detectives.

Claire Trent jumped in quickly. 'No. A waste of time. If he's the one who killed Marsland, he'll give himself away soon enough.'

Charlie Whitworth was about to continue, when the same detective asked a question. 'Are we any closer to finding out who was chasing Gerard Connelly?'

Everybody looked at Ridpath, including Claire Trent. She spoke quickly. 'We've put the E-Fit picture in the *Manchester Evening News* today and I've asked the local plod to do a thorough search of Sale Water Park. We're a bit stretched on resources at the moment but we need to keep following up. Everybody, and I mean everybody, will be pulling double shifts until this is sorted. Clear?'

A chorus of sighs and groans went round the room. Harry Makepeace muttered 'The missus will kill me.'

Claire Trent quietened the noise by raising her hand. 'Chrissy, do you have any news?'

The police support officer stood up. She was still wearing her Manchester City scarf around her neck, despite the room being uncomfortably warm. Ridpath wondered if she ever took the bloody thing off.

'Well, City won 5-1 yesterday...'

Another chorus of groans.

'So it wasn't a bad day. We're still top and the scum aka United are third.'

More groans. Chrissy smiled broadly before carrying on. 'We've been tracking activity on Gerard's mobile phone on the day before he vanished last week.' She pressed a key on the computer and a map of Manchester popped up on the screen. 'As you can see, we're looking at activity reported from cell masts. Smart phones send a regular signal to the nearest phone mast to help locate their position. We've plotted his route on the day he vanished.' She pressed another key and a red line appeared on the map. 'We have him leaving his home at noon on the day he disappeared. Having lunch in the Horse and Jockey pub with two friends and then driving into the centre of Manchester. We've correlated his cell mast hits with CCTV cameras on the roads and in the pub using ANPR.'

A series of pictures of a white Mercedes appeared on the screen found in car park, plus a couple of pictures of Gerard Connelly drinking and eating with friends.

'We checked the car. Nothing unusual. The last picture we have is from a street camera on Deansgate – it's very blurred I'm afraid.' Gerard Connelly was coming out of the Sawyers Arms with a woman by his side. The woman's face was hidden from the camera but she was tall and elegantly dressed.

'This was taken at 3:44 p.m. on Monday, April 16. The phone was switched off two minutes later.'

'Have we found the phone, Charlie?'

Charlie shook his head. 'Not yet, ma'am.'

'Who is the woman?'

'We don't know, guvnor.'

'Any CCTV in the bar?'

Chrissy sighed. 'There is, but it wasn't working. Under maintenance apparently.'

Claire Trent's eyes rolled back into her head. 'What's the point of CCTV if it isn't working? Any other pictures?'

'This is the best we have, guvnor.'

'Right, good work, Chrissy. Can you do exactly the same analysis of Phil Marsland's phone?'

'No problem, ma'am.' Chrissy sat back down.

As I say, the pathologist has promised me his full report on Phil Marsland today. We will meet tomorrow morning to take you through it. In the meantime, Charlie, I want you to follow up on the woman. Find out who she is and how she knows Gerard Connelly.'

'Yes, ma'am.'

'It's guvnor or Claire, Charlie, she said looking him directly in the eye. 'Chrissy, I want you to focus on the movements of Phil Marsland. He went missing on April 20.'

'Will do, guvnor.'

'Work closely with Alan on it. Robbo can you follow up on Liverpool? If we can stop the flow of guns into Manchester from the Scousers, we can prevent any retaliation from Big Terry.'

'Yes, boss.'

'Anybody got any questions?'

Ridpath thought about putting his hand up and telling them what he knew. But one look at Claire Trent's face told him the meeting was over. Her asking for questions was just habit. Anyway, everything he had was too vague at the moment and Claire Trent wouldn't thank him for revealing new information at a briefing if she hadn't been informed first. Whoever said 'knowledge is power' had obviously been a policeman at one time.

'Right, you lot. We need to keep the pressure up on these thugs. The sooner we solve these deaths, the sooner Manchester can get back to being the quiet rural backwater we all know and love.'

A few laughs from her audience.

'Well, what are you waiting for? Get out there and get working.'

## Chapter Fifty-Three

As soon as he was out of the meeting Ridpath rang Mrs Granger.

Still no answer.

This was worrying. He could imagine being out shopping with her neighbour on a Sunday afternoon, but early on a Monday morning? Surely the neighbour would be at work.

He thought about ringing the local plod and asking them to go round to check up on her, but with the state of their manpower at the moment, that might not happen until noon. Better go himself.

Just as he was about to leave, Charlie Whitworth collared him.

'In my office, now.' A finger pointed towards the bubble, the glass-sided room where Charlie could look out over all his detectives, making sure they were beavering away.

Inside, his boss didn't stand on ceremony.

'Not a word to anybody about Saturday night.'

'What happened on Saturday night?' Ridpath answered disingenuously.

Whitworth smiled. 'Good lad. Our Lady Master has put it down to coincidence at the moment.'

'She's not that stupid, Charlie.'

'I know, but I reckon she's too worried about the possibility of all-out gang warfare in Manchester to bother about a paedophile and his peccadilloes.'

'What happened to the kid?'

'As soon as the cops arrived the kid made his excuses and left, while Graham Connelly explained he wasn't married and didn't have a wife so there could be no possibility of domestic abuse.'

'Did he clock you were watching him?'

'Of course, he did. Stuck the finger up at us before he went to bed, didn't he? But you know what?'

Ridpath stayed silent, Charlie was going to tell anyway.

'I want these toe-rags to know we're watching them. The whole point is to prevent something happening, not to catch them in the process of doing it.'

'Won't they just wait until we run out of money for surveillance.'

Charlie's lips twisted beneath his moustache. 'Probably, but by then we will have caught the perps and locked them away.'

'I wouldn't bet on them surviving for long.'

'Good riddance to bad rubbish is what I say. At least it's not our problem.'

'You meeting Michael Connelly today?'

Ridpath nodded. 'Probably. Depends if the pathologist releases the body.'

'He should do. We'll get his report this afternoon.'

Ridpath thought about Dr Schofield. Should he tell Charlie about the links to the murder of Ronald Wilson? He decided to wait until he had interviewed the old woman. Wouldn't hurt to give him a little taster though.

'I may have something interesting for you this afternoon, Charlie.'

'About Connelly?'

'Could be, I just want to check something out first.'

'Don't be a cock-teaser, Ridpath. Out with it.'

Ridpath held his hands up. 'Not yet, Charlie, let me check something first and then I'll get back to you this afternoon. I'd better be going now…'

He half-turned, trying to get away.

'On yer bike, then. And one thing, Ridpath…'

Ridpath turned back to face him.

'I want to be the first one to know what you're up to. Don't go thinking you can butter your bread with Queen Trent. New information on this case is for my ears only. Understand?'

Knowledge is bloody power, thought Ridpath, but he answered, 'Of course, Charlie...'

'Of course, Charlie,' his boss mimicked. 'What are you waiting for? Don't you have a job to do?'

## Chapter Fifty-Four

Ridpath parked the car outside the grey house. The net curtains were drawn across the windows and everything looked as quiet as when he last visited Mrs Granger.

He knocked on the door.

No answer.

He peered through the curtains into the living room but couldn't see anything except his reflection staring back at him. There seemed to be a light on but he couldn't be sure.

Again, he knocked on the door.

Still no answer.

An old lady walked past wheeling a shopping trolley. 'You'll have to knock harder, love, she's bit hard of hearing is Mrs Granger.'

'Have you seen her lately?'

The woman stopped. 'She doesn't get out much. Her knees you know. Shocking bad they are. I had a hip operation myself last year. Those doctors had me up and walking in five days. My son calls me the bionic woman.'

'So you haven't seen Mrs Granger in the last few days.'

'No, love, but she'll be in there. You just have to knock louder.'

The woman trundled off, waddling from side to side, dragging her empty shopping trolley behind her.

Ridpath knocked again as loud as he could. He bent down and opened the letter box to shout through it. 'Mrs Granger, it's me, DI Ridpath.'

Still no response.

Was she out?

He thought back to when he last saw her, leaning on her Zimmer frame as she told him where to put the tea and the sugar in her kitchen. The woman wasn't going far.

But the memory sparked an idea in him. The kitchen backed on to a small yard with a back alley behind it. He ran to the corner of the street, spotting the back alley behind the houses twenty yards away. He ran down the alley, dodging over a suitcase full of dirty clothes spilling over the cobblestones.

Which house was Mrs Granger's? Luckily most of them had also painted their rear walls. The grey, bare walls of her home stood out sharply against the bright colours of the rest of the terrace.

He stood on tiptoes to peer over the brick wall. The yard was quiet and there was no movement in the kitchen. He rattled the back gate. It was firmly closed with a shiny new Yale lock. When did she have this installed?

He thought about using his shoulder to barge through but then decided it would be easier to climb over the six foot high brick wall.

He stepped back, took a running jump onto the wall and hoisted himself up so he was sitting astride the top.

Inside the kitchen all was still dark and quiet.

He was about to jump down when a voice shouted from above.

'Oi, what do you think you're doing?'

A fat, unshaven man wearing a string vest was leaning outside the upstairs window two doors down.

Ridpath reached into his jacket, pulling out his ID. 'DI Ridpath, working for the Coroner's Office. I need to speak to Mrs Granger.'

'Have you tried knocking on the door?'

'There's no answer. Have you seen her recently?'

The man shook his head. 'Not for a week or so. Do you want me to come down?'

Ridpath shook his head. 'Let me handle it, sir.'

He jumped off the wall and walked to the back door, peering in through the kitchen window. No sign of any movement.

He got out his mobile and rang her number one more time. He could hear the phone ringing in the living room but there was still no answer. Perhaps, she was upstairs in bed asleep?

But he remembered her telling him she didn't sleep very much anymore, the slightest noise waking her up.

'We haven't seen her for a while.'

A woman was shouting to him from the same window as the man.

'Is the old dear OK?'

Ridpath decided he should wait no longer. The back door had another new Yale lock, He took out his wallet and chose an old credit card he kept for this possibility. He slid the credit card between the lock and the door jamb, working it until he could feel the card against the bolt. He slid it up and pushed with his shoulder. The door opened wide.

'Mrs Granger? Mrs Granger?' He called from the door. 'It's DI Ridpath, anybody home?'

He could hear something in the front room. On the draining counter of the kitchen, two used mugs sat rim-down. He walked slowly forward. Next to them a kitchen knife, its stain-less steel gleaming in the light from the window and a smear of something red across the blade. 'Mrs Granger?' he said quietly.

Still no answer.

He reached the door of the living room. 'Anybody home?'

The room was dark, with only the soft light of the television illuminating it. He could hear the hectoring voice of Jeremy Kyle, shouting. 'We know you're the father, admit it!'

He pushed the door fully open.

Mrs Granger was sitting where he had last seen her, in the arm chair next to the fire, a knitting needle at her feet. Next to her, an untouched bowl of microwaved salmon and mug of tea stood on the low table.

Her green eyes stared out unseeing at the flickering television and a pink wash of dried blood bathed the front of her blue cardigan from the gash across her throat.

## Chapter Fifty-Five

It took the police less than seven minutes to respond to Ridpath's call. He thought he heard a tone of 'Oh, it's you again' when he rang dispatch but he probably imagined it.

The sergeant who came, an old pro called McNally, handled everything with a calm efficiency, rapidly blocking off the street and the back alley.

The neighbours came out in force to gawk at what was happening, with the fat man in the string vest and his thin wife at the front.

Tommy Harper eventually turned up after fifteen minutes, sucking a polo mint to unsuccessfully cover the tang of beer on his breath.

'You discovered her, Ridpath?'

'Yeah, at 10:22 a.m.'

'Why were you here?'

'Following up on Ronald Wilson's death for the coroner.'

'Why?'

'The coroner wasn't happy with your report of accidental death. Neither was the pathologist.'

'Shit, that's all I need.'

'The pathologist thinks Wilson was murdered.'

Harper's head went down.

'I think Mrs Granger knew more about what happened than she let on.'

'She didn't say a word to me when she ID'd the body,' Harper said defensively.

'Did you question her?'

'Why would I? She was there to ID her son who had drowned. Why would I ask her if anybody wanted to kill him?'

'But you didn't ask her anything?'

'Did you? You said you were coming to see her. Did you ask her?'

Ridpath shook his head. 'Didn't know it was a murder, did I?'

'Neither did I.'

The scene of crime van appeared at the end of the street. From the front seat stepped a tall, emaciated figure in a white suit who Ridpath recognised. Protheroe.

'Morning, Ridpath, you're turning up like a bad penny at these things.'

'You're the second person to notice.'

'Did you discover the body?'

Ridpath nodded.

Protheroe turned to one of his assistants. 'Make sure you take DI Ridpath's fingerprints before he leaves.'

'Yes, sir.'

'Well, in we go. DS Harper please ensure nobody comes in or out of the house without signing the register. And can you clear these people back another fifty yards, we want to bring up the other van closer to the house.'

'Will do. When can I see the body?'

'When I've declared it dead and completed a preliminary examination. After I've finished I'll call you.' Protheroe signalled for his assistant to come forward, pulling up his hood at the same time.

As they disappeared into the house, Tommy Harper said, 'What a charming man. I won't be inviting him to join me for a pint.'

'He wouldn't accept anyway, he's teetotal.'

'Teetotal?' Tommy spat the word out like it was a lump of cat vomit. 'Why would anybody be teetotal?'

'You could ask him.'

'I don't know if I'd like the answer.'

Behind them a group of constables from the local nick was pushing the crowd back and extending the perimeter with police tape.

'You'd better interview me, Tommy. Get it over and done with. Do you mind if I ring Charlie Whitworth before we start?'

'He's coming here?' Tommy adjusted his tie and straightened the collar of his shirt.

'Perhaps.'

'Did you mention what I asked you?'

'I did. But you better talk to him yourself if he comes.'

Ridpath pulled his phone out of his pocket wandering a few yards away from Tommy Harper until he was just about of earshot.

'DCI Whitworth,' Charlie's voice came on the line.

'It's me, Ridpath. I've got some bad news.'

'What is it? Not the cancer?' For once, Ridpath heard genuine concern in Charlie's voice. Perhaps the hard, unfeeling, male was just an act?

'I've just discovered the murder of an old woman, a Mrs Granger. A case I'm working on for the coroner.'

'Then it's a job for the local nick, not MIT. We've got enough on our plate.'

'I think you'd better come down.'

'Who's the local copper?'

'Tommy Harper.'

'Good luck then hold his hand so he doesn't balls it up.' He could feel his boss wanting to put down the phone.

'Charlie, wait. I think the murder is related to the death of Gerard Connelly.'

'How? Is this another one of your long shots, Ridpath? Can it wait till tomorrow? We've just received reports of a load of firearms coming in from Liverpool for Big Terry this evening.'

Ridpath thought for a moment. A meeting tomorrow would allow him to question the pathologist, Schofield, and bring Margaret Challinor up to speed. 'How about tomorrow morning? I'll come to the office and brief you.'

'That's good. There's a meeting at nine. Brief me before then.'

'Have you received the pathologist reports on Gerard Connelly and Phil Marsland yet?'

'Protheroe's has come in, but Schofield says he's working on something else. Stupid tosser hasn't worked out this is the most important thing we have at the moment. Claire Trent is giving him a kicking as we speak. She's handy with her high heels.' He paused for a moment before continuing, 'Anyway. I've got to go.'

'See you tomorrow, Charlie.' But the dead tone was already buzzing in his ears.

Tommy Harper stepped forward but Ridpath stopped him by holding up a single finger. He rang the pathologist's number but the phone was engaged. He then dialled Margaret Challinor and was put straight through.

'Mrs Challinor, Ridpath here. I've got some bad news. Mrs Granger, the grandmother of Ronald Wilson, has been found dead. Can I come and brief you this evening?'

'I'll be here until seven tonight. After that, I have a concert at the Halle. Rachmaninov.'

'Ok, I'll be there by 5:30. See you then.'

'Can't you tell me about it now, Ridpath.'

'I need to brief you properly. See you at 5:30. 'He clicked off the phone before she could ask him any more questions, turning back to Tommy Harper. 'I'm all yours.'

'Shall we do it down the pub?' the detective asked.

## Chapter Fifty-Six

In the end the interview took place in Ridpath's car. Tommy asked all the correct questions, giving him a written statement on the discovery of the body.

Strangely enough, Tommy was quite good at getting at the details.

'Did he notice any strange smells?'

'Did he touch the victim?'

'When did he first see the knife?'

'What time was it on the clock?'

'Did he notice anything unusual in the kitchen? In the living room?'

Then Tommy started chewing the end of his pen. 'Just a few more questions, if I may.'

Ridpath checked his watch. 'Fire away.'

'You said you interviewed her on Friday afternoon?'

'That's right, I left at 5:30 p.m. to meet my wife and daughter.'

'But you came back on Saturday morning.'

'I dropped in to her house at eight a.m. before going to a briefing with Claire Trent. She was alive when I left her on Saturday morning around 8:30.'

'What were you doing here on Saturday morning?' There was an edge to Tommy's voice.

'I came round to give her some groceries. I noticed she didn't have anything to eat in the house when I interviewed her on Friday.'

'Bit of a Good Samaritan are you? Didn't know that was part of the coroner's officer job?'

'It isn't. I felt sorry for her. I also rang social services but it was obvious they weren't going to get anybody out to see her until today at the earliest.'

'Did anybody come?'

'You'll have to check, Tommy.'

The detective sergeant chewed the end of his pen again. 'So you were the last person to see her alive and the first person to see her dead.'

'No, Tommy, the first person to see her dead was the murderer, not me.'

There was a tap on the window of the car. Protheroe stood outside with the hood off his head but still dressed in his protective suit. Ridpath wound the window down.

'I've completed the initial examination and pronounced her dead. Don't quote me but I'd say she's been dead for less than twenty-four hours, probably between twelve to twenty hours.'

'So sometime on Sunday?' Tommy asked.

'That's where I would put it. I may be able to give you a more exact time after the post-mortem. The fire was on, which may have sped up the process of decomposition.'

'Anything else, doctor?' asked Ridpath.

'A couple of things. The lividity of the body suggests she was killed where she sat and has not been moved. The cause of death was probably loss of blood, but I need to check in the post-mortem, just in case.'

'And the weapon?' asked Tommy.

'The bread knife in the kitchen has obvious blood caught in its serrated edge. But once again, let's wait until the post-mortem and DNA tests on the blood before we jump to conclusions. I'll go back in and finish off. We'll bring the body out in about half an hour, so you'd better warn the uniforms.'

Ridpath glanced over his shoulder. In the time he had been giving his statement the crowd had swollen; kids, mothers, fathers and grannies were all pressing against the police tape trying to see what was happening.

'Here you go, Ridpath, you'd better sign and initial this. Let me check your mobile number in case I need to get in touch with you.'

Ridpath took the form and signed it, saying 'I'm free to go, am I, Tommy?'

The detective sergeant didn't join in the joke, simply answering. 'For the moment, Ridpath, for the moment.'

A fleeting image of Elsie Granger telling him to bless himself with holy water raced across his mind. 'I'm going to get whoever did it, Tommy, no matter what it takes. No old woman deserves to die like this.'

# Chapter Fifty-Seven

Leaving Tommy Harper to organise the crime scene, Ridpath drove slowly through the crowd and parked up around the corner. He rang Dr Schofield, once again only getting through to an irritated voicemail message. 'I'm busy right now. Please leave a message and I'll get back to you sometime in the next millennium. Beeeeeep.'

Ridpath switched off his mobile.

This case was becoming complicated, he had to clear it up in his own mind before he briefed the head coroner. He spent the next ten minutes jotting down a few notes and trying to connect the dots. It soon became obvious how many gaps there were in his knowledge of the victims.

There must be something linking them.

But what was it?

His dashboard clock said 4:55 p.m. If he drove quickly he would just make it in time to meet Margaret Challinor. He put the car in gear and sped away from the pavement, nearly running over a poodle playing in the street.

'Concentrate, Ridpath,' he admonished himself. The last thing he needed now was a bloody car accident.

Driving carefully he arrived at Stockfield Coroner's Court ten minutes late. He hurried into the coroner's office, past a startled Jenny who was just packing her stuff to go home.

'You're late, Ridpath,' was the coroner's greeting as he entered her office.

'Sorry, Mrs Challinor, I was giving a statement.'

'Sit down. I've got an hour before I have to leave.'

Ridpath pulled out the bentwood chair in front of her desk, feeling like an errant schoolboy about to be chastised by a stern headmistress. He put out his notes on her desk and gathered his thoughts.

'When you're ready, Ridpath, perish the thought you would actually brief me before midnight.'

'The case has become complicated, Mrs Challinor. I've just left Mrs Granger's house. She was murdered sometime on Saturday.'

'Murdered? Who would want to kill an old lady?'

'Somebody did. And I think this death is linked to those of her grandson and of Gerard Connelly.'

'Go on…'

'Let's start with Ronald Wilson. According to the pathologist he was killed and his body dumped in the lake…'

'Correct. The police belief it was a tragic accident or suicide was totally wrong.'

'Agreed. But I noticed a connection between Ronald Wilson's murder and the death of Gerard Connelly.'

The coroner sat forward, a frown appearing between her elegantly shaped eyebrows. 'What connection? One was stabbed in the head, the other was run over by a lorry.'

Ridpath raised his hand and began counting off his fingers. 'Firstly, both were only dressed in blue boxer shorts.'

'It's common enough, I would guess about 30 per cent of men wear them.'

'Actually, it's 58 per cent, I checked. The shorts were brand new and none of them had been washed. Most men wear them for at least four years. You'll be pleased to hear one in ten men only change their underwear once a week.'

'Not a pleasant thought, Ridpath, but what's your point? Is it just a coincidence both men were wearing brand new blue boxer shorts?'

'To answer you, briefly, I don't think so. There are too many other coincidences in this case.'

'Explain what you mean.'

'I checked the ante-mortem injuries on both bodies. After reading the pathologist's report on Ronald Wilson and the possible rope marks found on his wrists, it reminded me of Dr Schofield's findings on Gerard Connelly. I asked him to compare them.'

'And?'

'I'm still waiting for a response.'

Mrs Challinor tilted her head. 'Let's ring him now.'

She pressed the speaker on her phone and speed dialled the pathologist. Ridpath listened to the warbles and squeaks as the phone connected, expecting to hear the click of the answering machine kicking in.

Instead, Dr Schofield answered immediately. 'Coroner, I was just about to call you.'

'I hope it was with good news, doctor.'

'Good and bad, I'm afraid.'

'I have Ridpath sitting next to me and you're on speaker phone.'

'Good, saves me repeating my message to him.'

'I believe he asked you to perform a comparison of the injuries on the bodies of Ronald Wilson and Gerard Connelly.'

'That's correct, Mrs Challinor. I have performed the comparison and there are surprising similarities between the two clients.'

'Can you elucidate, doctor?'

'The scarring on Gerard Connelly's body shows sixteen sites of interest. There may have been more but, as you know, parts of the body were severely damaged by the lorry. An examination of the left wrist which was undamaged in the accident shows the presence of partially healed rope scarring. Under a microscope I noted that the fibres of hemp still adhered to the skin. An examination of Ronald Wilson's wrists showed a comparative morphology despite the body having been in the water for at least ten days. Again, under the microscope, hemp fibres were found subcutaneously.'

253

'All it proves is that both men were tied up, doctor, not that they were tied up by the same person.'

'True, Mrs Challinor However, there is a startling similarity between the fibres.'

'You're saying they came from the same type of rope?'

'I'm saying more, Mrs Challinor. In the fibres found on Gerard Connelly's left wrist I found some of the fibres contained DNA.'

'Of course they do. They will have been in contact with his skin?'

'But it's not his DNA, coroner.'

Ridpath could almost hear the drum roll at the other end of the phone.

'I compared the DNA with that of Ronald Wilson...' The pathologist paused for a few seconds.

'And?' asked Margaret Challinor.

'It was a match.'

Ridpath leant closer to the phone. 'I'm sorry, I don't understand.'

'It means both Ronald Wilson and Gerard Connelly were both tied up, or came into contact with, the same rope. Do keep up, Ridpath.'

'Exactly, Mrs Challinor. And that's the link between the two deaths.'

The coroner was silent for a moment. 'Thank you, Dr Schofield, this throws a whole new light on our investigation.'

'It's so good to talk to someone who understands the latest developments in forensic science, Mrs Challinor.'

'But why?' interrupted Ridpath.

'Why what?' answered the coroner.

'Why did he tie them both up?'

'I think it is your job to find out, Ridpath, don't you? Do you have any other questions for Dr Schofield?'

'Just one more. Do you know Dr Protheroe?'

'Jim? Of course.'

Ridpath didn't know Protheroe's first name was Jim. 'He's the pathologist on two other murders that may be related to the case. Those of Phil Marsland and Elsie Granger. Could you share your findings with him?'

'You think the cases are linked, Ridpath?' asked Mrs Challinor.

'Possibly. Phil Marsland was tied up and dressed in boxer shorts too before being murdered. The science may be able to tell us.'

'Finally, you're speaking like a scientist rather than a copper,' a high-pitched laugh echoed down the phone line, 'I'll share my findings with Jim after this call.'

'Anything else, Ridpath?'

He shook his head.

'Thank you, doctor.'

'I'll be adding these discoveries in an addendum to my post-mortem report.'

'Thank you, doctor. I'll see you again in the near future,' added Margaret Challinor.

'Call me when you are free.'

She clicked off the speaker phone.

'A new relationship with the pathologist, Mrs Challinor?'

'Not at all, Ridpath. I merely explained to him how incon-venient it was if his reports did not arrive in time for my inquest.'

'Your chat must have worked, he seems eager to please. Less irascible.'

'I also may have casually mentioned having recommended Dr Schofield for the position with the Trust, I could also unrec-ommend him. He took the hint.'

'A smart young man.' Ridpath was about to make another joke about being young, then didn't. It was definitely not the right time.

'So, what are your next steps? The inquest on Ronald Wilson will reopen on Thursday.'

'Can you postpone?'

'Possibly, but we have already empanelled a jury. I felt this case had implications for police competence and should be decided by a jury. So, next steps?'

'I'm going to brief Detective Superintendent Trent and DCI Whitworth tomorrow. This discovery impacts their investigation into the death of Gerard Connelly.'

'Fine, but I asked what are you going to do, not what are you going to tell people.'

'If you would let me finish, Mrs Challinor...'

She held up her hands. 'Sorry, Ridpath. I'm becoming impatient. If we don't have the answers before Thursday then I am going to postpone the inquest again, re-empanel the jury and reschedule for a later date. After the Harold Lardner case the Ministry of Justice is already looking over my shoulder, threatening an audit of my performance as a coroner.'

'I am aware of the issues, Mrs Challinor. But after listening to the pathologist, I feel sure that there is also a link to the murder of Mrs Granger and Phil Marsland.' Ridpath scratched his head. 'It's like we're peeling back the layers of an onion and all we've removed so far is the outer skin. Charlie Whitworth told me a couple of days ago of an old mantra used by detectives. Why plus what equals who. We don't know why they are being killed, neither do we know what for. Until we do we'll never find the who.'

'You don't buy MIT's theory of a gang war?'

He shook his head. 'Why fight now? They are all making money, their differences have been sorted and they're busy diversifying into legitimate business like taxis, security and property. A gang war at this time would be bad for business. It's what Michael Connelly pointed out to me three days ago.'

So what are you going to do?'

'Next step is to contact Tommy Harper.'

'That waste of oxygen...'

'He's a smarter copper than you think, Mrs Challinor. More importantly, he needs help at the moment and he has access to the police files on Ronald Wilson, Gerard Connelly, Phil Marsland and Elsie Granger.'

'You want to see if they knew each other?'

'Something like that. There must be link between all four, we just haven't found it yet.'

Mrs Challinor looked at her watch. 'You'd better get a move on, Ridpath. You have just one day, fourteen hours and forty-six minutes till my inquest opens on Thursday.'

# Chapter Fifty-Eight

Tommy was pleased to hear his voice. 'You didn't leave your dabs with the SOCO, Ridpath.'

'You want me to come over now?'

'Could do. No pub for me tonight. Have to make sure all the paperwork is up to date.'

'I need your help, Tommy.'

'Somebody asking for my help, that's a new one. Usually I'm told what to do.'

'Well, this could help put you in Charlie Whitworth's good books.'

'I heard Dave Hardy's leaving?'

News travels fast on the tom-toms of the police concrete jungle. 'Yeah, I heard the same rumour.'

'But, Trent wants a woman.'

'You know Charlie, he'll appoint somebody who he likes.'

'You mean somebody who's loyal to him.' After a pause, Tommy asked suspiciously, 'What do you want me to do?'

'Nothing, Tommy, It's what I want us to do.'

'Why does my hair tingle when you use the word "us"?'

'You're not using the right shampoo, Tommy. Head and Shoulders works wonders for the old scalp itch. Or you could try washing it in a pint of Tetleys.'

'Waste of a good pint.'

'Tell you what, I'll see you in thirty minutes at Reddish nick. How's that?'

'Time to grab a meat and potato pie from the local chippy.'

'You've got to eat a little more healthily, Tommy.' Fine words from a man who hadn't had anything to eat today except a Starbucks coffee this morning. Ridpath had been counselled on his diet by a dietician as part of his recovery programme from the myeloma. For three months, with Polly's help, he had kept to it religiously. Since she had left he had fallen by the wayside. Not eating stodge or fast food, but basically not eating at all. 'I'll pick up a sandwich from Pret for us both.'

'I like the BLT.'

'You would.'

On his way to Poynton, Ridpath picked up the sandwiches and dropped into a chemists for the shampoo. Time to butter up Tommy with a bit of soft soap, he chuckled to himself.

The detective sergeant was waiting for him in the lobby of Reddish Police Station.

'I hope you brought the brown sauce. Can't eat bacon without brown sauce.'

'Brown sauce is not one of your five a day, Tommy.'

'It is in Salford.'

There was no answer so Ridpath didn't bother. They went to Tommy's desk. There was no time for small talk, Ridpath simply told the detective what he wanted.

'But it'll take hours going through all those old files.'

'You doing anything better tonight?'

'Can I get Maureen to help?'

'Maureen?'

'The PCSO, she'll know where everything's kept.'

'Hasn't she gone home already?'

'Not Maureen, lives here, she does. What she doesn't know ain't worth knowing.'

He shouted across the CID room. Hidden behind the desk in the corner was a short, thin woman wearing the thickest glasses Ridpath had ever seen and a silver cross hanging around her neck.

'Maureen, can you help us for a minute?'

She walked across to the two detectives.

'This is DI Ridpath from MIT.'

She shook out her hand. 'You work with Chrissy?' she asked.

'Used to, now on secondment to the Coroner's Office.'

'Bit of a comedown for an MIT detective isn't it?'

Tommy coughed. 'Maureen, we need all the files on Ronald Wilson…'

'The one who topped himself at the Secret Lake?'

'That's him. His old charge sheets, warrants and any intelligence in the Police National Computer or HOLMES about him.'

'Right, give me ten minutes, I'll print it out.'

'Plus, we want the latest intelligence on Gerard Connelly and Phil Marsland. Anything and everything on the PNC.'

'Sure, let me get you the Wilson files first.'

Maureen was a good as her word. Just as the detectives were finishing their sandwiches, she appeared holding three folders.

'Ronald Wilson's arrest warrants and trial documentation,' she put the first folder down. 'His intelligence in the computer, not much here I'm afraid. Bit of a tearaway when he was young but nothing since he came out of prison.'

Ridpath grabbed the arrest file and began reading. Tommy Harper slowly took the intelligence file.

'Thank you, Maureen for finding them for me,' she said.

Ridpath looked up. 'Sorry, I'm a bit under the cosh. Thanks for these.'

'That's OK, DI Ridpath, I've worked here for twenty-seven years. I recognise management putting the squeeze on.' She tried to go, then stopped.

'What is it?'

'Wilson. The name rings a bell. Let me just check something, won't be a tick.'

Ridpath returned to Ronald Wilson's file. A few minor run-ins with the law; shoplifting, dope possession, being in a stolen car, but nothing major until 2014. He was then charged with GBH. A fight down a pub turned ugly and somebody was glassed. Wilson was sentenced in 2015 and sent down for three years serving his time in Leeds and Warrington prisons. He would check Gerard Connelly and Phil Marsland's file later to see if they had been locked up together. Was that the connection?

'You ever heard of a Peter Avery?'

Tommy Harper looked up from his file. 'Yeah, put him away a couple of years ago. Minor con artist and low life. Caught receiving and it was his fifth conviction. Still in Strangeways, I think. I got the impression he preferred being in prison to being outside. Thought it was safer.'

'He was Wilson's victim in the pub attack, gave him a cut needing fifteen stitches. Is Avery the sort to seek revenge?'

Tommy shook his head. 'Nah, he will have put it down as the price of doing business. He must have stiffed Wilson over some stuff he was fencing.'

Well that was one theory to cross off the list. Ridpath returned to the file. The address for Ronald Wilson was the same as Mrs Granger. His probation officer was a Chris Ryan. Maybe give him a bell tomorrow.

He turned the page. Empty. That was it.

Ronald Wilson, this is your life of crime. No Eamonn Andrews coming through the door with a big red book though, just a few bits of paper in an old file. Not terribly successful even when he was a criminal and nothing since he was released in 2017. The old woman's story seemed to be holding up. 'Anything from intelligence?'

'Not a lot. Ran around with gangs when he was young.'

'Anybody we know?'

Harper shook his head again. 'Nah, just the usual low lifes stealing cars and dealing drugs. There's a note from his probation officer, a Miss Ryan. 'Ronald Wilson is adjusting to life outside of prison. He's yet to hold down a steady job but works on a casual basis. There have been no reports of consorting with his old confederates. He has kept all his appointments with me. The next steps are to find him a steady job. He seems to be open to this idea.'

'Confederates?'

'You can't get the staff these days. Ms Ryan must have just been appointed, straight from university. You think he was pulling the wool over her mortar board?

'Nah, fits in with what his grandmother said. He was trying to go straight.'

Tommy closed his file and threw it down on the desk. 'Not a lot of use then.'

Ridpath agreed. 'I need more details about the family. Did Ronald Wilson have a brother?'

There was a cough from behind. Maureen was standing there holding a much thicker file. 'I've printed this for you, thought it might be useful.'

'What is it?' asked Ridpath.

'His dad's file.'

'His dad?'

'Harry Wilson. A major villain in the nineties. Was shot dead in 1995. Thought you knew...'

## Chapter Fifty-Nine

After the killing of Elsie Granger, there was a palpable air of excitement about both of them. Reggie had been cleaning and checking both the Uzi and the Armalite obsessively, caressing the matt black metal of each of the guns, oiling the barrels, checking the balance of both of them and the fit against his shoulder.

'They're good,' he finally announced, 'Both have been looked after by somebody who knows what he's doing.' Four years in the army as an armourer had given him a confidence around weaponry.

His sister, on the other hand, had been pacing up and down the kitchen, going over the details in her mind. They had worn gloves so there was no possibility of leaving prints in the old woman's house on Sunday, but they could have left something behind; a blonde hair, fibres from her jacket, a shoe imprint in the blood from Elsie Granger.

She shrugged her shoulders. Why was she wasting so much time worrying? It didn't really matter. By the time they finished today, a gang war would have started in Manchester. The Connellys versus Big Terry. No holds barred. No quarter given. A vicious, bloody war where she and her brother were going to be the only winners.

For a moment a chill swept down her body. Had she thought of everything? She stopped pacing the kitchen and turned to her brother. 'You know what you have to do?'

He slotted the magazine into the Uzi for the umpteenth time. 'Yes,' was the single word answer.

'What are you going to use?'

He looked at both weapons lying on the kitchen table next to the bowl of sugar and a bottle of brown sauce. 'The Uzi. It will be quicker and more effective, with less chance of collateral damage. The velocity of the bullet...'

'Fine,' she interrupted him, but be careful when you attack. This must be seen as an amateur job not a professional.'

'Sure.'

'The police?'

'Outside the taxi shed. I'll drive past them.'

The last detail bothered her. What if one of them was actually awake and watching. Would they remember her brother? 'Are you sure? It's not necessary.'

He picked up the Uzi and unfolded the metal stock. 'No, but it amuses me. They will remember the car and it will put the fear of God in them.'

'Be careful.'

'I will. You'll come here later?'

'As soon as I can get away.'

'You've arranged the weapons for Big Terry?'

'They'll arrive tonight. The Connellys received theirs this morning.'

'We're set then.'

'All it needs is a tiny spark...'

He held up the Uzi. 'Or one of these.'

# Chapter Sixty

Ridpath remembered his manners this time. He said thank you before grabbing the folder. It was a case file on the murder of Harry Wilson, September 22, 1995. At the top the word 'UNSOLVED' was stamped in bright red letters.

'I printed it out from the cold case registry. Apparently, they've been looking into it again without too much success.'

'Maureen, can you check up on Ronald Wilson's family? Did he have a brother? And what was the name of the mother?'

'I'll check the birth and marriage records. We have the name of the father so it should be possible online. I can even check the electoral register for the period.'

'Great.'

Ridpath opened the file. It was the usual pro forma opened for every case. The investigating officer was a DI Ted Roylance. Ridpath had never heard of him. 'Do you know a Ted Roylance, Tommy?

'Yeah, detective inspector, retired about ten years ago. Why?'

'Any good?'

'Old school. Bit of a plodder but a good copper.'

Ridpath began reading the report. The usual bumf about the Police and Criminal Justice Act 1967 was followed by a report disclaimer. 'This statement consisting of (one page signed by me) is true to the best of my knowledge and belief and I have made it knowing that, if it is tendered in evidence, I shall be liable to prosecution if I have knowingly stated in it anything I know to be false or do not believe to be true.'

Ridpath had read a million of these in his time. This one was well written and precise, with the typing showing it was done on one of the old typewriters.

Statement of Edward Roylance
Occupation: Detective Sergeant, A Division, Greater Manchester Police
Number: 23756
Date 23 September 1995

At 15:25 hours on Wednesday, 22 September 1995, I received a call to attend to an incident at the Davenport Arms, Corporation Street, Manchester. On arrival, I found the body of a forty-two-year-old male lying face down on the floor of the saloon bar. He had two gunshot wounds. One to the chest and the other to the back of the head. Two spent cartridge cases from an automatic pistol were present on the floor of the pub.

Subsequent enquiries revealed this man was Harold Wilson (DOB 12.5.54.) The first attending officer on the scene, Constable Ian Jack (PC 4006) had arrived to find the man already dead at 15:06 hours. The shooting incident had happened eight minutes previously with a barman, Mr David West, reporting the incident to the control centre at 15:02 hours.

The pathologist was called and a scene of crime team arrived at 16:02 hours. Prior to their arrival the public house was sealed off and witnesses to the incident were detained to provide statements.

The following statements were taken and are appended to this document:

Mrs Doreen Wilson (DOB 14.6.63) – wife of the deceased
Mr David West (DOB 12.12.72) – barman

Mr Stan Havers (DOB 08.11.46) – friend
Mr Lance Gibbs (DOB 02.3.48) – friend
Mr Liam Livingstone (DOB 01.1.70) – friend
Mr Michael Connelly (DOB 04.4.56) – friend

These were the only people present in the bar during the incident.

The pathologist, Mr Harold Lardner, pronounced Mr Wilson dead at 16:45 hours. The body was removed to the mortuary for a post-mortem at 17:12 hours.

The pub remained closed while the scene of crime officers examined the premises for evidence.

Signed and dated. Edward Roylance

Ridpath's eyes widened as he noticed the last witness name. He flicked forward to Michael Connelly's witness statement.

# Chapter Sixty-One

What did it all mean?

He read through the statement once again. It was typed and from the mistake with the broken 'p', Roylance had obviously used the same typewriter as his own report.

WITNESS STATEMENT
(CJ Act 1967, s 9 MC Act 1980, ss. 5A(3)(a) and 5B, MC Rules 1981, r70)

Statement of: Michael Connelly
DOB: 04.04.56
Occupation: Businessman

I was drinking in the Davenport Public House with my best friend, Harry Wilson. We had all met up in the pub at approximately noon time, the event being arranged the night before. Only Lance Gibbs arrived late about one p.m. We were celebrating the signing of a new business deal to open up a club. Harry was to be the owner and the other three of us were investors. We had a few pints and then moved onto the whiskies with Harry buying more than a few rounds.

The area where we were sitting was empty with just our group occupying the main table. This wasn't unusual as Harry was a regular in this pub and had asked Dave, the barman, to keep people away from our area.

The time in the pub had been happy with Harry and his wife, Doreen, in particularly good form.

Around 2:55, I am not sure of the exact time as I didn't look at my watch, a man entered the room on my left. Harry shouted 'Oi, what you doing here, this is a private party.' The man then said, 'Shut your mouth Harry, you've said enough.' At which point, he drew a gun and fired at Harry hitting him in the chest.

I upended the table spilling all the drinks and used it as a cover to protect myself. I don't know what the others did but I heard Doreen screaming loudly. Then, the man walked over to Harry, who was lying on the floor, and fired one more shot into his head.

The noise was deafening and the next time I looked the man was gone. Harry was still lying on the floor with blood pouring out of his head and pooling on the lino and the broken glass. Doreen was still screaming.

I shouted at Dave to call the police which he did. I then went to Harry and checked his body. A large hole was in the back of his head with blood pouring out of it. I went to comfort Doreen and was doing this when a constable arrived.

I do not know what the others were doing when the gunman was shooting. I have helped to create a description of the man, but my memory of his face is not very good as I was staring at the gun in his hand.

Signed: Michael Connelly 23.09.95

Ridpath then read all the other witness statements and documents relating to the case, handing them across to Tommy Harper as he finished them.

Ted Roylance had done a competent if not very imaginative investigation. Everything was done by the book, all the 'I's dotted and the 'T's crossed, but still no arrest.

Three things struck Ridpath immediately. The killing was obviously planned; the killer knew exactly where they were going to be even though the meeting had only been arranged the night before. Secondly, the killer knew Harry Wilson's identity, calling out his name before shooting him. Thirdly, it was a professional hit. The killer calmly walking over to Harry Wilson's body and shooting him in the back of the head to finish him off.

Professional killings were always the hardest to solve. There was no motive, no connection with the victim and often no link to any previous crime. No wonder Ted Roylance had been unable to pin it on anybody.

Ridpath finished reading the file and waited for Tommy Harper. 'What do you think?'

'Gang leader gets executed in pub. It's a bit Al Capone, ain't it?'

'They didn't call it Gunchester for nothing.'

'Ted Roylance didn't make a collar.'

'Not surprising. Looks like a contract killer to me. But who hired him?'

'If I remember correctly, didn't this killing start the whole war off? The Salford, Gooch Close, Cheetham Hill, and other mobs all getting involved. Bloody mayhem, it was.'

Ridpath narrowed his eyes. 'I think you're right. Wasn't it over security on the clubs of Manchester, with the doormen controlling the drugs trade? I'll have to check it.'

Maureen was standing next to him. It was amazing how quietly and invisibly she glided around the station as if she were part of it.

'I checked the births, marriages and deaths site for Harry Wilson. I can tell you the exact dates if you want them by calling the registry in the morning. But I can tell you from the index that he married a Doreen Granger sometime between April and June 1993.'

'Makes sense, then. Elsie Granger was the mother-in-law,' said Ridpath.

'They had a daughter soon afterwards, Christine, born between October and December of 1993.'

'A shotgun wedding?'

Maureen ignored Tommy Harper, continuing to read from her notes.

'They also had two sons, but you'll never guess what they were?'

Maureen was obviously one of those who enjoyed information being teased out of her. Ridpath stroked the stubble on his face. 'Enlighten me.'

'Twins. Born sometime between April and June 1995. Their names were Ronald George and Reginald Michael Wilson.'

'Ronald George Wilson? Is that our vic in the Secret Lake?'

Ridpath nodded. 'Ronnie and Reggie were also the Christian names of the Kray Twins.'

'The East London gangsters?' asked Maureen.

'Why would Harry Wilson name his sons after two of the most violent gangsters Britain has ever known?'

'That's a good question, Tommy. But a better one would be what happened to Reginald Wilson?'

# Chapter Sixty-Two

It was late when Ridpath finally reached home. Maureen had rummaged around in the records but couldn't find anything new on the Wilson murder. She had managed to dig up a birth announcement from an archived copy of the *Manchester Evening News*.

> *Harry and Doreen Wilson are excited to announce the arrival of twin sons, Ronald and Reginald, born on April 2, 1995. Mum is tired but very happy. Dad is drunk. Two are always better than one.*

She had also dug up a few articles from the period. The *Manchester Evening News* prided itself on its crime coverage. The fact that lurid stories of rapes, murders, assaults and arrests sold tons of newspapers was neither here nor there.

This one's headline was a classic:

> *'Suspected gang leader meets violent death'*

> *One of the alleged leaders of Manchester's most violent gangs, Harry Wilson, met his own nemesis in the shape of two lead bullets fired from an automatic pistol yesterday. At three in the afternoon the assailant, wearing a dark blue hat on his head, walked into the Davenport on Deansgate, took out his gun and shot the alleged gang mastermind twice, once in the chest and again in the head.*

*The gang leader was pronounced dead at the scene by the pathologist of Manchester Royal Infirmary, Harold Lardner. A paramedic at the scene said, 'With those injuries nobody was going to survive.'*

*Witnesses to the incident report the killer moved quickly and the time from him entering the pub to the death of Harry Wilson was less than one minute.*

*Liam Livingstone, a friend of Mr Wilson said, 'We were having a quiet drink in the back room of the bar when in walked this man and shot Harry dead. He didn't stand a chance, but we're going to get who did it. Nobody gets away with this.'*

*Detective Sergeant Edward Roylance, leading the investigation appealed for calm, saying. 'The police will find out who committed this dastardly crime and when we do, they will be put away for a long time. This crime has all the hallmarks of a professional operation.'*

*The Manchester Evening News has since learnt that the killer drove away in a green Ford Mondeo, licence plate M478 RWQ. The car was later found abandoned in the Gorton district of Manchester.*

*If any witnesses saw the incident or have anything to report, please call the hotline on 865-1111.*

Next to the report was a picture of the pub, the Davenport. A year later it was severely damaged when the IRA planted a bomb in the centre of Manchester blowing out the beautiful stained glass windows that had survived a hundred years of drunks, fights and the best the Nazis could throw at them.

Beneath that was another picture. This time of a woman with her head down, obviously distraught, being escorted by a uniformed police officer. It was captioned 'Doreen Wilson being led away from the scene of the crime by police.'

By the time Maureen found this it was already eleven p.m. Tommy decided he'd had enough and went home. Ridpath followed soon afterwards. Now here he was, back in an empty house, it definitely wasn't a home.

Ridpath yawned and stretched, throwing his bag down on the floor. He was tired, more tired than he had ever felt before.

He walked over to the cabinet and poured himself a generous serving of Laphroaig, adding just a splash of water for the health of it. As if by magic, the glass rose to his lips and he took a large mouthful. A shiver ran through his body and he suddenly trembled with cold. Not the normal reaction to a dram of Scotland's best.

Tired, too tired.

He switched on the heating and sat down. How could he get everything clear in his mind? At the moment there were far too many questions and far too few answers.

Who killed Elsie Granger? And why?

There seemed to be no point. She was an old lady, incapable of hurting anybody. Jesus, she even struggled to make herself a cup of tea. So why kill her? There had to be a reason.

Could she have told Ridpath more?

Probably.

A deep slash to the throat was sure to silence her for good.

He kicked himself. Why didn't he ask her more questions? Why had he been more concerned that she drank a cup of tea rather than doing his job as a copper?

Then he remembered he wasn't a copper any more but a coroner's officer. He raised his whisky in the air, seeing the honey coloured liquid through the squares of the cut glass. 'Cheers, Charlie.'

He took another big mouthful, feeling the heat as it slipped down his throat and a sharp pain as he swallowed. Strange, there seemed to be no taste. He touched his nose to the side of the glass.

He couldn't smell anything. Usually, the whisky was over-powering with the scent of peat and malt and honey and the sea.

Now nothing.

He sneezed twice and a shiver wracked his bones. Was the loss of smell due to the tablets? He would ask Dr Morris at his next check-up. Or was he going down with a cold or flu? If it was the latter, he should report to the doctor at Christies. But they might take him for observation and then what would happen to the case? Nobody else would follow it up and Tommy Harper was as useless as a wet Wednesday in Accrington.

He'd take a few paracetamol and drink the Vitamin C Polly had bought for him. Make himself a hot whisky before he went to bed. And, Bob's your uncle, he would be right as rain in the morning.

He couldn't stop the investigation. Not now he was so close. And somebody had to find Elsie Granger's killer. Old women should be allowed to live out their days in peace not suffer attacks by mindless thugs.

His mind flashed back to that day on the M60. It felt like years ago, but less than six days had passed since the incident.

What was the link to the death of Gerard Connelly? The same rope had been used by the kidnapper in both cases. Was it Reginald Wilson?

As a twin of his brother Ronald, it would explain the likeness in the photographs. The pictures of the dead Ronald were the spitting image of the man with the gun.

At least they knew he had been murdered now. It wasn't just an accident on the motorway. Was the killing of Phil Marsland revenge for Gerard's death or was there another reason?

How did the death of Harry Wilson fit into all this? It happened over twenty years ago, yet it seemed to run through the case like words through a stick of Blackpool rock.

None of it made any sense.

He took another long gulp of whisky. A shiver ran down his spine again, but this time of pleasure rather than cold. What was Charlie up to now? Was he still staking out Graham Connelly? Watching over him like a wolf guarding lambs?

As the whisky took over his tired mind and his eyes began to droop, another thought raced around his head.

Elsie Granger had taken care of Ronald Wilson after his father's death, but what had happened to the other children, Reginald and Christine?

And more, where had their mother gone?

# Day Seven

*Tuesday, April 24, 2018*

# Chapter Sixty-Three

Ridpath woke up to find himself still sitting in the chair, the whisky tumbler lying at his feet and the aroma of stale alcohol in the air. Light was pouring in through the curtains.

*What time is it?*

The clock on the mantelpiece said 6:35 a.m. What time had he fallen asleep?

He stretched his neck left and right, hearing the tendons click. The muscles of his legs ached where they had been pressed against the arm chair. The heating was still on and he was tired, grumpy and feeling sorry for himself.

He picked up the glass and walked to the kitchen to put the kettle on. His stomach rumbled. Had he eaten yesterday? A sandwich from Pret a Manger with Tommy Harper and umpteen cups of coffee. A bacon sandwich would work a treat.

He opened the fridge. Inside was a half pack of margarine, a shrivelled apple and the milk smelt like it was off.

Worse than Elsie Granger's fridge. At least, she had an excuse.

Black coffee it was going to be then. He looked around the kitchen for the jar. Where did Polly keep it? Nothing in the cupboards except tins of spaghetti hoops, Eve's favourites. He thought about opening one but the idea of them for breakfast made his stomach churn. The rest of the cupboard was filled with assorted packets of cereal, dried spices well past their sell-by date and packets of Polly's favourite instant noodles.

His body felt tired and his head heavy and swollen. Had he drunk a lot of the Laphroaig last night? He only remembered drinking one glass before he fell asleep.

Sod this for a game of soldiers. He would pick up something from the canteen and go to the supermarket when he had five minutes. Why he didn't buy anything when he had been shopping for Mrs Granger escaped him.

He showered, changed his clothes and was in the car in thirty minutes. On went David Bowie and *Jean Genie*; he needed something to give him some energy before facing Charlie Whitworth.

After twenty minutes of the thin white dude he was ready to face the world. The life enhancing properties of a couple of bacon sarnies and he would be all set for the day.

He just stepped into police HQ, when Charlie met him at the lifts.

'You've been a bad little soldier, Ridpath.'

'What?'

'Come with me. Madam is waiting for you in her office.'

'Claire Trent?'

'Who else?'

They walked into the lift, getting out on the MIT floor. Ridpath was dying to ask Charlie what it was all about, but his boss just stared straight ahead at the polished aluminium of the lift door.

They walked across the detectives' floor. Most people were already at their desks, tapping away on their old PCs. A few raised their eyes as Ridpath walked past, but quickly dropped them again.

Why did this feel like a scene from the *Green Mile*? Another dead man walking?

Charlie tapped on the door, heard a brisk 'Enter' from inside and opened it, gesturing for Ridpath to go in first.

Claire Trent was sitting behind her desk, make-up as immaculate as ever and a mountain of papers and reports in front of her.

'When were you going to tell me, Ridpath?'

## Chapter Sixty-Four

He placed the Uzi in the black holdall along with three extra mags just in case he needed them. He was only planning to use one mag, but you never knew what was going to happen.

The 6P mantra drilled into his brain during his army training had stayed with him. Piss Poor Planning Prevents Proper Performance.

'Are you ready?' she asked.

'Locked and loaded.'

She put on her coat. 'Right, let's get going. I'll leave the car on Moorside Road in Urmston. You can pick it up and dump the one you stole yesterday there. Leave the keys in the ignition. With a bit of luck the local kids will nick it and lead our friends in the police a merry chase. I'll put a whisper on the street to let them know.'

He stood up and kissed her on the forehead. 'You've already told me the plan ten times.'

'Eleven doesn't hurt.'

He pushed a blonde hair off her forehead. 'You're nervous?'

She nodded.

'Why? We've done all the planning, nothing can go wrong. We've got them all at each other's throats and killing the old lady removed any links to our past.'

'It's just... it's the last step. If we get this right, then we can sit back and watch them kill each other.' She reached out and touched his cheek.

'You're going to enjoy that?'

'You have no idea how much. It's time to pay them all back for the death of our father. The delivery of arms will go through?'

'Big Terry should get them tonight.'

She smiled. 'Moss Side and Cheetham Hill are primed and waiting?'

'We've been feeding them both arms for the last six months. Nothing too good. Just a few old Makarovs to tempt them. The good stuff will come in the next few days.'

'Courtesy of Dominguez's partners?'

'Former partners. We are their new retailers in the UK.'

She moved away. 'It's all just business to them. But for us, it's far more than that.'

'After today Connelly will have to move quickly.'

'But he won't. He's too old now, too slow, not like before.'

'What about Graham?'

She sniggered. 'Graham. A wet fart in a blanket. Gerard was the smart one and without him they are lost.' She opened the door. 'Time for me to go. I'll see you tonight?'

'I'll be here waiting.'

'Reggie, take the other route, don't drive past the police. No point in taking chances, not now.'

'Sure, if that's what you want.'

'It's better.' She nodded once and then left.

He checked his watch. He would leave exactly at 10:30 a.m. ETA on target at 11:00 a.m. Change cars at 11:07 a.m. Home again 11:35 a.m. Cars fuelled and checked. Satnav disabled. Don't want them to find out where he came from.

He smiled to himself. He would drive past the police in their shitty silver Vauxhall Vectra. He had to have some fun in life, despite what his sister said. What was the point of doing anything, unless there was some thrill involved, a chance of being caught?

But the thrill only worked if you were prepared.

6Ps. Remember them.

He took the Uzi out of the holdall. Time for one last check.

## Chapter Sixty-Five

'I don't know what you mean, guvnor.'

'Don't "guvnor" me, Ridpath, not when you've been holding back information.'

'With all due respect, ma'am, I didn't hold back any information.'

'That's not what Tommy Harper told me this morning.'

So the fat toe-rag had tried to ingratiate himself by calling Claire Trent and telling her everything they had discovered last night. 'Can I sit down?'

She nodded.

He pulled out a chair. 'I haven't told you yet because I'm still not sure we are onto anything.'

'A mistake, Ridpath. Your job is to keep me informed, not keep me in the dark. The message from Tommy Harper was so garbled as to be unintelligible. Something about a gangland killing twenty years ago.'

So the beer belly on legs couldn't even get his facts straight. 'I was going to let DCI Whitworth know this morning...'

'Really?' said Claire Trent, her eyes rolling upward. Then you'd better tell *me* now what you think you have discovered.'

'DI Ridpath arranged to meet me before the briefing, ma'am.' At least, Charlie was defending him.

'So?' She checked her watch. 'We have three minutes before the briefing starts. What's going on, Ridpath?'

He took a deep breath. His career was hanging by a thread here. If he made one wrong move, Claire Trent would have him working in lost property for the rest of his life. A fate worse than death.

'Margaret Challinor asked me to look into the death of a man called Ronald Wilson. His body was found in Wingate Lake just over a week ago...'

'What's this got to do with our gangs?'

'I'm getting there.' He sneezed twice. Claire Trent handed him a box of tissues from her desk. He wiped his nose and continued, 'She felt the death was suspicious. The police report was inconclusive; either suicide or an accident. But she felt something was wrong.'

'She has good instincts does Margaret Challinor.'

'The pathologist's report stated Ronald Wilson was murdered; a stab wound in the brain.'

'This is all very good but how does it impact the case we are working on right now...?'

Ridpath held his hand up. He felt another sneeze coming on but stifled it. 'I noticed some links between the Wilson case and the death of Gerard Connelly. Both were semi-naked when found, both just wearing blue boxers. Both had ingested a sleeping drug, Ambien. And both had rope marks on their wrists.'

'It's very tenuous, Ridpath, even for you. CPS would throw the case out before it went to court.'

'That's why I asked the pathologist, Dr Schofield, to compare and contrast the two men to see if there were any links in the way they died.'

'And were there?'

Ridpath nodded. 'He found the rope marks on both men to be similar...'

'Similar is not evidence, Ridpath.' Charlie Whitworth interrupted.

'I haven't finished yet. He also found Ronald Wilson's DNA on minute rope fibres discovered on Gerard Connelly's body.'

Claire Trent leant forward in her chair, 'Go on.'

'That's it really. It shows the same rope was used to bind both men. And if the same rope was used...'

'Then they were tied up by the same person. The two cases are linked.' She sat back again. 'But there's no link between the two deaths. As you said, one was stabbed in the brain, the other run over. Have you considered the samples could have been cross contaminated? They were both analysed in the same lab. Plus surely the amount of DNA would have been very small. Has Schofield performed verification tests?'

Ridpath sat there staring into mid-air. It was a possibility. He hadn't thought to ask Schofield about verification tests. If the DNA did come from laboratory contamination then all his assumptions were wrong...'

The slamming shut of Claire Trent's desk diary brought Ridpath rapidly back to the office in police HQ. 'It's not enough. We have a briefing right now...'

'I also asked him to liaise with Protheroe to see if there was a link with the murder of Phil Marsland and of Ronald Wilson's grandmother, Elsie Granger,' Ridpath stammered a reply.

'Hang on a minute. You're saying that you think all these cases are linked? One person has been killing all these people?' Charlie was suddenly animated.

Ridpath took another deep breath. Why did he feel so tired, it's like all his bones were aching. 'I have come to that conclusion, yes.'

'Where's your proof?'

'I don't have any yet. It's just an educated guess. I'll know more this afternoon, when Protheroe reports.'

Charlie sat back. 'You've got nothing. You're just wasting our time, Ridpath.'

Claire Trent held out her hand to stop the DCI from speaking. 'But why, Ridpath? If these deaths are linked, as you say, there must be a reason?'

'I'm not sure, ma'am. I think it's to do with the murder of a man called Harry Wilson twenty years ago,'

'Hang on, Harry Wilson? Wasn't he shot dead in a pub on Corporation Street? They never found the killer.'

'I think he was Ronald Wilson's father.'

Charlie Whitworth closed his eyes, shaking his head. 'It makes no sense, Ridpath, why would anybody kill the son of a man shot dead twenty years ago?'

There was an urgent knock on the door. The detective constable who drove Claire Trent entered without waiting for an answer. 'Sorry to disturb, guvnor, but the briefing is ready to start.'

She nodded at him before turning back to Ridpath. 'Look, I've got two of Manchester's biggest gangs ready to start all-out war. As we speak, both Big Terry and Michael Connelly are looking for guns to start killing each other. I have a chief constable breathing down my neck demanding results. I have all the district commanders screaming about overtime bills.' She picked up a few sheets of paper from her desk and waved them in the air. 'And to top it all off, I've just had both the police commissioner and the mayor of Manchester on the phone, who dislike each other with a vengeance. They both decided to bury the hatchet this morning, and stick it into my head instead.' She smiled at him, her lips colourless. 'So forgive me, but I really don't have time for your little theories at the moment. Some of us have real policing to do.'

'But I think I'm on to something, ma'am.'

She stood up. 'Come on, Charlie. We'll make this briefing short and then you and I are going to have a chat with Michael Connelly. It's time to defuse the tension and let him know we're watching his every move.'

'What do you want me to do?' asked Ridpath.

She looked him up and down. 'I'd get that cold seeing to if I were you, and go back to the coroner's office. I'm sure she can find something to keep you busy. Or you could go home. You look like death warmed up, Ridpath, take a few days off.' She ended the conversation without a trace of sympathy in her voice.

And then Claire Trent and Charlie were gone, leaving Ridpath alone in the office. Through the window he could see the wasteland known as North Manchester; ugly prefabricated warehouses, a few isolated pubs, neon-red fast food shops, patches of bare ground where once had stood rows and rows of terraced houses, despair hanging on every street corner.

He wasn't giving up. He was onto something, he could feel it in his aching bones.

But what was he going to do next?

## Chapter Sixty-Six

Ridpath walked into Reddish station after first stopping at Tesco's to pick up some cough sweets for his sore throat and packets of paper tissues for his briefcase.

He hadn't stayed long at HQ. He'd walked past the briefing room hearing Claire Trent's voice lecturing the team. For a second he thought about going in, but then decided against it. She had been quite clear, go back to work for the coroner or go home.

He walked out and sat in his car without starting the engine. He knew he was on to something. His whole body screamed there was a link between the deaths of Ronald Wilson and Gerard Connelly, with more possible links to the murders of Phil Marsland and Elsie Granger.

He knew there was something there. The pathologists' reports may find a link but there had to be something else. He couldn't go back to Stockfield to sit in front of his desk, knowing he was so close.

He started the engine, remembering an old trick his old mentor, Sergeant McEwan had taught him. 'If you're stuck, laddie, follow your instincts. They'll tell you where to go in any investigation.'

That was why he was going back to Reddish station. He had to follow up on Elsie Granger's family and the murder of Harry Wilson.

There was something there, he knew it in his water.

For a change the reception area was neat and tidy. 'Is Tommy Harper in?'

The duty sergeant was classic old school. 'Who shall I say is asking?'

'DI Ridpath, coroner's officer.' It felt strange saying those words after his name when it should have been, DI Ridpath, Major Incident Team. 'I was here last night,' he added to cover his own embarrassment.

The sergeant made the phone call. 'Apparently he's not in yet. Must be out on something.'

'Is Maureen here. It's her I want to talk to anyway.'

'She's always here. Let me buzz you through.'

The door clicked and Ridpath walked through. Somebody had cleaned the place up after last night. Gone were the Pret wrappers and coffee cups. Maureen was standing beside her desk. She was wearing the same clothes as last night.

He pointed to her. 'Haven't you been home?'

'These are my work clothes. Wouldn't be seen dead in these on the street. Keep them in the locker and change every morning. But I think you forgot the first sentence.'

Ridpath's eyebrows raised.

'The one about "Good morning, Maureen, did you sleep well?".'

'Oh that one. Well, did you?'

'No, not really. I was thinking about this case.'

'Come up with anything?'

She smiled and beckoned him over to look at her computer. 'I got in early and rang a friend at the registry office. I'm a bit of family historian in my spare time. She's just sent me these details for Doreen Wilson.'

Ridpath peered over her shoulder to a see marriage certificate on the screen.

'Doreen Wilson married again. A man called David Stokes in Fleet, down south in Hampshire.'

'Well away from Manchester.'

'You couldn't go much further.'

Ridpath checked the date on the certificate. 'August 12, 1996. That was quick, less than a year after the death of her first husband.'

Could she be the woman with Gerard Connolly in the CCTV picture? And perhaps the mysterious woman who had called in Ronald Wilson's supposed suicide attempt, despite the fact he had been stabbed and his body dumped? The woman who wouldn't give her name and the police still hadn't found. Could it be a woman behind this, getting revenge for the murder of her husband over twenty years ago, using her son to carry it out? But why wait till now?

Maureen interrupted his thoughts. 'I checked up on a Doreen Stokes in Fleet and this came up.'

She pressed the enter key and a newspaper obituary appeared on the screen. The words were in the depressing format full of commas so loved by obituary writers:

> *Stokes, Doreen. After a long illness, the death is announced of Doreen on October 4, 2014, aged 51, loving wife to David Stokes and mother to Christine, and the twins, Ronald and Reginald. May she rest in peace.*

'Are you sure this is the same woman?'

'Her age and name are correct, plus who else would have three children with exactly the same Christian names with two of them being twins?'

She had a point. So if Doreen wasn't the woman who had reported Ronald's body in the lake, who was?

Ridpath glanced across at the PCSO sitting in front of her computer. The thin woman's body was shaking with excitement.

'So, after I saw this obituary, I went on Facebook and searched.'

'What for?'

'I checked if Doreen Stokes had a Facebook page.'

'But she's dead…'

'Most people don't take them down. There are thousands of dead people on Facebook.'

'And not many living either.'

'She did.' Maureen sat back in her chair.

'Don't leave it at that. Tell me...'

'Here it is.'

A Facebook page appeared on the computer. A woman's picture was displayed prominently in the header. The face was smiling and happy, so different from the face in the *Manchester Evening News* on the day of the murder, but it was the same person there could be no doubt.

'So we've now found out what she looked like before she died, so what?'

Maureen held up her finger. 'That's where I was clever. I searched her list of friends...'

'And?'

'This name came up.' Maureen moved her cursor over a name and a small picture.

'Reggie Stokes,' said Ridpath.

'They taught you how to read in training school, detective.' Maureen clicked on the name and she was taken to another Facebook page with a large picture as its header.

Ridpath whistled. 'What the...'

# Chapter Sixty-Seven

He didn't know why he did it.

Adrenalin perhaps.

The sound of the bullets hitting the glass and brick.

The jolt of the Uzi against his shoulder.

Whatever. It didn't matter. For the first time in a long while, he felt the power of sheer joy.

He had driven past the taxi shed, taking a good look at the goons standing in front of it. On the left, the silver police Vauxhall was parked, two coppers sitting inside looking like the plastic dummies they were.

Then he had turned left, driven slowly down the street and stopped in front of Michael Connelly's house. The Uzi was out of the holdall and lying next to him in the passenger seat.

He had opened the window, checking the area around the house as his sister had told him to do.

Nobody.

Perfect.

He had picked up the Uzi, flicking off the safety switch and checking it was on automatic.

Starting at the top windows, he had kept his finger on the trigger, hearing the burp of the gun and feeling the judder against his shoulder.

The glass in the windows shattered, crashing to the floor, the bullets thudding into the surrounding brickwork giving off little puffs of dust as they hit home. For a second he wished he had brought the Armalite too. He would have had fun with its .223 Nolsers.

He heard the loud click as the magazine emptied. Should he load one more?

He checked the house. All the windows were shattered on the top floor and most on the ground floor.

Enough. He had made his statement. And besides, he had another idea. His sister would probably kill him, but he just had to do it.

The icing on the cake.

He put the car in gear turning left at the end of the road instead of right as he should have done. The car would still be waiting where his sister had left it. It wasn't going anywhere.

He drove slowly, hearing the sirens of the police cars as they raced to Michael Connelly's house. Two passed him going the other way, with their sirens blaring and grim-faced police sitting in front.

Keystone Kops.

He made another left and stopped, checking his watch. He would wait here for five minutes before making the attack.

He checked the Uzi. The barrel was hot, but it would be ok. He removed the spent magazine and pulled out a new one from the holdall, slotting it into place.

Shame, his sister had told him to leave it in the car. Perhaps, he would take it with him. Such a beautifully balanced weapon, a waste to just throw it away.

He would handle his sister.

No problem.

After all, she needed him. She *still* needed him.

He checked his watch again.

11:01 a.m.

He must have made the attack slightly early. No matter. It meant he would be five minutes late dumping this car and picking up his own but it was within permissible operational parameters. And besides, he couldn't give up this chance. It would have far greater effect than simply shooting up the house.

He checked the Uzi once again, wiping it down and taking out the mag, looking at the bullets nestling inside their metal casing before slotting the mag back into the machine pistol.

11:04 a.m.

A few more minutes and it would be time to go. They would all be at the house by now, running down from the taxi shed after the noise of gunfire. All milling around, staring at the damage and chaos he had created with one small Uzi.

In the hands of a professional, it could be deadly.

As he was about to show them.

He switched the Uzi over to firing bursts rather than automatic and laid it on the seat next to him.

11:08 a.m. Time to go again.

He put the car in gear and drove to the end of the road, turning left once again. One big circle had brought him back to the edge of the park.

At the next corner was the taxi shed with its cars parked illegally on the grass verges. He drove slowly towards it.

Outside, a tall bald–headed man in a leather jacket stood looking at his phone.

Stupid bugger, shouldn't be here. He should have run to the Connelly's house like the rest of them.

No matter.

His loss.

The man smiled to himself. His loss of life in this case.

He rolled down the window and pointed the Uzi straight at the man, feeling the bullets leave the end of the muzzle and rip into the leather jacket.

Again and again and again.

The man fell backwards, his body smashing into the green wood of the taxi shed, before sliding slowly down to the ground.

He flicked the switch back to automatic and sprayed the rest of the magazine at the shed, watching the wood splinter and dance as the bullets struck home.

God, he loved this. The sheer beauty of a rifle in the hands of a man who knew how to use it. The sound of glass shattering. The thud of bullets into wood. The jolt of the recoil as the Uzi jerked in the grip of his hands.

It felt good to be alive.

Now to really piss them off.

# Chapter Sixty-Eight

They were already close to Michael Connelly's when Charlie received the phone call.

'Right. How long ago? Five minutes. We're on our way.' He pulled the mobile phone away from his ear and spoke to Claire Trent. 'Somebody just shot up Michael Connelly's house.'

'Shit. Just what we needed,' She ran her fingers through her hair. 'Any injuries?'

Charlie asked the switchboard. 'None reported,' he answered.

She leant forward and touched her driver's shoulder. 'How long to the house, Alan?'

He checked the satnav. 'About ten minutes.'

'Make it quicker. Use the siren.'

The dashboard lights began to flash and the car surged forward, throwing both Charlie and Claire Trent backwards into their seats.

They arrived outside Michael Connelly's house seven minutes later.

The place was in an uproar. Thugs with bald heads were running around. Graham Connelly was screaming at the top of his voice. Neighbours were gawking through their windows, a few at the end of their gardens peering over the privet hedges.

The brickwork of the house was covered in small holes and nearly all the windows were shattered. Broken glass lay in lumps all over the garden.

A uniformed sergeant ran to their car as it slid to a stop. 'I've set up a road block at the other end of the street to prevent vehicles coming down. Armed tactical units are on their way plus back-ups from Eccles, but we're a bit stretched at the moment.'

The sergeant had spoken directly to Charlie Whitworth but it was Claire Trent that answered. 'Make sure you block off both ends of the street, I don't want anybody else near here unless they are in uniform. OK?'

'Yes, ma'am'

As he was speaking, a puffing and panting Dave Hardy and Harry Makepeace ran across to the car. 'We ran down from the surveillance car. We've checked the area and the shooter has gone.'

'Anybody see what happened?' she said stepping out of the car.

'There's one eye witness. A Mrs Conroy.'

A middle-aged woman was standing on the pavement her arms across her extensive chest, looking bored as if the arrival of a fleet of police cars was the most normal thing in the world.

Graham Connelly was still shouting at the top of his voice. More thugs were running to join him in the garden, their feet slipping and sliding on the broken glass.

Claire Trent went to the rear of her car, opening her boot. She reached in and took out two stab vests with the word 'Police' stencilled across the back. 'Put this on.'

He looked at it. 'Too small.'

'Never mind. Put it on.'

Charlie struggled with the fastenings but eventually managed to clip the vest across his stomach.

'You go with Dave Hardy and check at the Connelly's. See if anybody was injured.'

'Yes, ma'am.'

Claire Trent walked over to the witness, reaching inside her jacket pocket for her warrant card. 'Detective Superintendent Trent. I believe you witnessed the event.'

The woman nodded.

Across the street, Graham Connelly was screaming orders at the thugs who were still running around like headless chickens.

'Can you tell me what happened?' Claire Trent asked again as she was joined by the uniformed sergeant and Alan, her driver.

'I was just about to go down to the shops. I shut the door and walked to the end of the garden path. A car stopped outside Michael's house and there was a loud noise, like an exhaust popping. The windows started to explode and I heard the bullets hitting the brickwork. Well I got down on the ground as soon as I worked out what was happening. Not right, is it? Michael's such a lovely man and been on his own since Carmen died.'

Claire Trent looked down at her feet. 'Let's just start again from the beginning shall we? You were going to the shops? What time was this?'

'About eleven. I'd just heard the beeps on the radio and shouted for my son to get out of bed otherwise he'd be late for work, his shift starts at noon. He's a lazy one, he is, and is gonna lose his job, but he don't care. Twenty-six years old and still living at home…'

'So at eleven you reached the end of your path. Which house?'

'Behind me, number twelve, diagonally opposite Michael and Carmen, God bless her soul.'

'And Michael Connelly lives at number seven.'

The woman nodded. 'Just him and his daughter, Carmela. Graham stays there sometimes, but I don't see him much. I think he's got his own place in town. Wish my bloody useless son would move out too.'

'So a car pulled up outside the house. What sort of car?'

'A white one.'

'What make of car?'

'I dunno. Quite big. A BMW or summat like that. I don't know cars from Adam.'

'OK, a car drove up. How many people in it?'

'I can't remember. You're asking too many questions. It does me head in.'

Claire Trent reached over and touched the woman on the arm. Don't worry, Mrs Conroy, you're doing great. We have to ask these questions I'm afraid and it's always best when the events are fresh in everyone's mind.'

Behind her, the squeal of brakes. A transit van had stopped next to where the sergeant had stretched tape to block the road. The leading officer, carrying a Heckler and Koch across his chest, approached her.

'Inspector Hurd, Armed Tactical Unit. You're the senior officer, ma'am?'

'I am. Take your men and seal both ends of the street. DCI Whitworth is at the house now. The suspect is in a white car but we believe he's already left the scene.

'Yes, ma'am.'

His men fanned out behind him like a well-drilled army unit.

Claire Trent turned back to Mrs Conroy. 'Just a few more questions, OK?'

Mrs Conroy nodded.

'How many people were in the car.'

'Just the one I think. The driver.'

'Did you see his face?'

She shook her head. 'No, after I heard the shots I got on the floor. When I looked up again the car was gone.'

'Which way did it go?'

'It must have gone towards the other end of the street because I didn't hear it come past me. That's the way he was facing anyway.'

'Can you give a statement to this detective, DC Alan Johnson.'

'Will it take long? Only I've got to get my husband's tea and he don't half give me gyp if his snap ain't on the table when he gets home.'

But Claire Trent was already walking across to where Charlie was staring up at Michael Connelly's house.

He glanced across at her as she arrived. 'Looks like at least thirty shots. A sub-machine gun is my bet. Low calibre I would guess. See, not much impact on the brick.'

The front door opened and Michael Connelly peered out. Instantly, his son ran to his side. He stepped through the door with his arm around the shoulders of his daughter. Her head was down, the shoulders trembling with fear.

'Where's the bloody ambulance? We called the bloody ambulance years ago.'

As if on cue, in the distance the wail of an ambulance was approaching.

'Look at her.' Michael Connelly shouted. 'She could have been killed. My daughter could have been killed. Where were you lot? Tell me that. Where were you lot when Terry Marsland was shooting up my house?'

'Calm down, Mr Connelly, the ambulance is on its way.'

'Calm down? Calm Down? You're telling me to calm down?' He let go of his daughter and raced towards Claire Trent as if to attack her. Charlie and Dave Hardy stepped in front of their boss as she shied away, wrapping their arms around Michael Connelly.

'You want a charge of assault too, you stupid old bastard. One more step and I'll have you in the nick so quick your feet won't touch the floor.'

He pushed Michael Connelly back towards his daughter.

The ambulance turned the corner and drove through the crowds of people that had begun to gather from the neighbourhood, drawn like vultures to carrion. It approached the police tape slowly, was allowed through and parked outside the house. Two medics ran out and one placed a blanket around Carmela Connolly's shoulders before leading her to the back of the vehicle.

'Go with your daughter, Mr Connelly. You're more use to her than you are here,' said Claire Trent.

Graham got hold of his father. 'Go with Carmela, Dad Me and the lads will look after the house.'

'You were supposed to be looking after it before.' He gestured up at the broken windows. 'Look at it! This was your mother's house. Look at it.'

'I'll get whoever did it, Dad. I'll make them pay. But now, you need to go with Carmela, she needs you.' He called two thugs forward. 'Stay with my dad, make sure nobody gets close to him or my sister.'

Reluctantly, Michael Connelly followed the ambulance men. As he passed Charlie Whitworth, he leant over and whispered. 'That's the last time you lay your hands on me, Whitworth, understand?'

He walked to the ambulance followed by the two thugs.

'DCI Whitworth to me.' Claire Trent had moved to one side and was calling him to her.

Michael Connelly climbed into the back of the ambulance following his daughter. The two thugs got into a black Mercedes parked outside the house and started the engine

'DCI Whitworth.' Claire Trent was calling again.

He walked over to her as the ambulance pulled away, followed by the black Mercedes.

'Charlie, I want you to go back to HQ and co-ordinate the operation from there.'

'But I want to be here, ma'am.'

'No. I need somebody back at HQ, manning the phones and sorting out resources.'

'But, I'm always on the operations, it's my…'

Her jaw set. 'Don't argue. I'm giving you a direct order, DCI Whitworth. Go back to HQ.'

He looked around him. The house was covered in bullet holes, armed police lined the streets, flashing lights illuminating their faces in the grey light of the spring morning and he was being ordered back to HQ.

'Yes, ma'am, as you say, ma'am.' He strode away over to Dave Hardy. 'Your keys.' Dave handed them over. 'The car is still outside the taxi shed?'

'Yes, boss, but…'

Charlie Whitworth turned his back on his friend and marched up the road. The sooner he got out of here and away from that bitch the better.

# Chapter Sixty-Nine

She watched Charlie Whitworth's back as he walked up the road. He was a good copper but a major pain in the arse. As long as he was around, she would never get proper control of MIT, the men would constantly look towards him for orders rather than her.

And it was time to get control. Sending him back to HQ was just the beginning. From now on, Charlie Whitworth would toe the line or he would be out.

Alan was running towards her.

'We've a got hit, guvnor, a white car abandoned two miles away in Urmston. It might not be the one but it fits the description.'

'Send a team to check it out.'

Alan ran off to pass on the order.

'Scratch that, Alan,' she shouted after him, 'I'll go myself, bring the car.'

'Yes, guvnor.'

Dave Hardy was still standing around, staring forlornly after his boss. Time to get him working. 'Dave.' She called him to her.

He ran over. 'Yes, ma'am.' There it was again. Why couldn't he just call her guvnor? 'I'm going to check out a lead in Urmston. I want you to organise the SOC team when it arrives and makes sure the Armed Tactical Unit forms a proper cordon around the area.'

'Yes, ma'am.'

The car with Alan at the wheel raced up, coming to a stop at the kerb.

'Make sure all these thugs stay away from the area. I want it clear for the SOCOs.'

Dave Hardy looked over his shoulder. At least six thugs were standing in front of the bullet- shattered house, with more arriving, all being directed by Graham Connolly.

'And how am I supposed to do that, ma'am?'

'Use your charm, Dave. And if that doesn't work, arrest the bloody lot of them. This is now a crime scene.'

'Yes, ma'am'.

As Claire Trent was about to get into the back of her car, a sound like ripping fabric came from the end of the street.

'Gunfire!' shouted the inspector in charge of the tactical unit.

# Chapter Seventy

It was him.

The man on the motorway.

Ridpath leant in closer, staring at the Facebook page.

It was definitely him. He was dressed differently, in camouflage uniform, posing alongside two other soldiers, a rifle comfortably balanced on his hip. 'This is the man I saw on the motorway chasing after Gerard Connelly.'

'It's Reginald Stokes, or Reggie as he calls himself on Facebook. Looks like he had two tours of duty in Afghanistan, but he hasn't posted anything for the last six months. According to his Facebook page he left the army nine months ago. Do you want me to get on to them in Aldershot, they may have forwarding address for him.'

'Please do it, Maureen and thanks, the work is great.'

'Just doing the job.'

Ridpath sat down as Maureen picked up the phone.

He had to get everything straight in his head. He tapped his forehead. It was hot and he could feel a headache growing between his temples. One of those obscene headaches that expanded slowly to fill the brain.

He tapped his forehead twice, pulling the skin over the bridge of his nose as Polly had shown him. The Chinese way to get rid of a headache.

'It's all about Chi. There's a major energy pathway running through the nose to the brain.'

Ridpath didn't know about that but he pulled the skin anyway. For some reason it worked. Perhaps it was because the skin became so painful and bruised that it took his mind off the headache.

He forced himself to think about the case. Harry Wilson had been executed in a gangland killing in 1995. By 1996 Doreen Wilson had married again, moving down south with her new husband. That's what Elsie Granger had said and it checked out.

In the background Maureen was talking to somebody on the phone and then slammed it down, waited a few seconds, picked it up again and tapped out a new number.

He took out his notebook and began to write it down. He often found writing something laboriously in longhand forced him to slow down and lay things out clearly.

Harry Wilson and Doreen had three children. A girl, Christine, and a pair of twins, Ronald and Reginald. Ronald stayed with his grandmother and grandfather, living with them until he was sent to prison. It seemed Reginald had been taken by his mother to live with her new husband in Fleet in Hampshire, eventually joining the army. What had happened to him after he left the army nine months ago? Where did he go? He wrote down the questions on his pad.

Ridpath had definitely seen him beside the motorway chasing Gerard Connelly. Was he taking revenge for the murder of his father twenty-three years ago?

Maureen turned back to face him. 'The army are going to get back to me. At first they were playing bureaucratic buggers but I explained to them that this was a murder investigation with the possibility that this ex-soldier was about to murder again. If they didn't release the information, the newspapers would love to hear the story.'

'You were liberal with the truth, Maureen.'

The PCSO smiled broadly. 'I know, but they are going to get back to me in five minutes. I'll say a few Hail Marys at confession on Saturday. I'm sure God will forgive me.'

Ridpath glanced down at his notes. It all looked clear now. Only one thing bothered him.

Where was the girl?

What had happened to Christine? When the boys had been taken by the grandparents and the mother, where had the girl gone?

The phone rang.

It was immediately snatched up by Maureen, 'Right, go ahead.' She grabbed a pen and began writing on her pad. 'OK, great. This is his forwarding address and it's in Manchester?' She nodded her head. 'Thanks for this. You may just have saved somebody's life.'

She put the phone down, ripping the page from her notebook and handing it to Ridpath. 'This is the address they have, but I've never heard of it.'

Ridpath stared at the address written in Maureen's neat capitals. 'Never heard of it either. Can you pull up Google Maps and type the address in?'

Maureen opened her computer. A Google Map of Manchester appeared on her screen. She typed the address in the search box and the map began to zoom in on a red marker over a house.

It was right next to the M60 motorway in Sale Water Park.

'Jesus,' said Ridpath, 'that's the house I saw.'

He picked up his mobile and dialled Charlie. He had to let his boss know.

# Chapter Seventy-One

Bloody woman treating him like a young copper, fresh out of Sedgley Park. He had twenty years under his belt. Twenty years of hard graft to get to where he was now. Twenty years of late nights and long hours. Twenty years of working his bollocks off, living with the slime that was the criminals of Manchester. Twenty years of yes sir, no sir, three bloody bags full sir.

And all for what?

To be told to go back to HQ like a naughty boy and organise the bloody phones.

Charlie Whitworth kicked a stone lying in his path, sending it slamming into a parked car. Around him, people were milling on the other side of the police tape stretched across the road. Armed officers were standing behind the tape, their Heckler and Koch rifles across their chests and their funny little baseball caps worn at a jaunty angle.

Charlie forced himself through the crowd, ripping off his stab jacket.

Bastards. This is where he should be, not stuck in some bloody office behind a desk waiting for a phone to ring. He was an active officer not some pen-pusher, happy to wear a bloody uniform and pretend he was still doing vital police work moving forms in triplicate from one computer to another.

What had GMP become?

It wasn't a police force anymore. It was full of fast track university graduates who wouldn't know a criminal from a cream cake. All he ever wanted to do as a policeman was to lock up bad guys and keep them off the streets. But now the bosses were only concerned about window dressing for PR. They cared more about having police attend local community meetings, where the main complaint was about dogs fouling the pavements, than stopping real crime.

Sod the whole lot of them.

He shook his head like a dog shaking a rat.

Violent criminals are left to roam the streets because locking them up is too much bloody hard work. While good coppers, like himself and John Gorman, are forced to retire or put behind desks answering bloody phones.

The crowd was thinning out as he reached the top of the street. With all the police around, there was no need for the surveillance car anymore. He would drive it back to HQ and park himself in front of his desk just as she'd ordered, holding a phone in his sticky little mitt.

But it was time for a transfer. Time to find something else. Time to do real police work again.

Suddenly, the sound of a gun firing rapidly came from the right. Charlie lifted his head and listened for a second.

More firing coming from the direction of the taxi shed. Somebody was shooting up Michael Connelly's place. He ran round the corner.

Up front, a white car had stopped in front of the shed and was firing into it. Bullets were ripping into the wood, sending splinters flying, shattering the windows. One of the bodyguards was sitting with his back against the shed wall, blood pouring out of his chest.

For a second the bullets stopped firing and the car moved slowly forward, stopping next to the old Vauxhall Vectra, the police surveillance car.

The passenger window rolled down and a hail of bullets slammed into the metal of the car.

Charlie ran forward into the middle of the road, shouting. 'Police.'

The driver looked, turned his head, and stared straight at him. The muzzle of the gun vanished from sight.

For a second, time stood still. Then the car surged forward, accelerating straight towards him.

Charlie put his hands out in front, like a matador trying to stop a runaway bull.

But the car kept on going, getting closer and closer. Speeding up all the time.

Charlie tried to shout, but no words came out of his mouth. He tried to move his legs, to jump out of the way, but they wouldn't react, as if rooted to the tarmac of the road.

He was too old now.

Too slow.

The car was close, he could see the driver's face. A young man, eyes dark and empty. The face in Ridpath's E-Fit.

The same face.

He didn't feel anything when the bonnet of the car hit him.

Instead, he had the sensation of flying, of being free and soaring up and over the car.

For a moment, he looked down on himself, flying through the air, the car racing past him, his body upside down, one shoe slipping off to go in a completely different direction.

And then his body hit the hard concrete.

The air left his lungs. A sharp pain seared through his right leg.

All went dark.

The blackest black he had ever imagined.

# Chapter Seventy-Two

'With me.' Claire Trent shouted the order and began running towards the gunfire.

Dave Hardy was slightly ahead of her, surprisingly fast for an obese man. On her right, the inspector in charge of the armed response team and two of his men were slightly behind but running quickly.

The crowd who had been quietly watching the events outside Michael Connelly's house were now screaming; some running back to their homes, some throwing themselves to the ground. A young child, no more than four years old, was crying at the top of his voice, his eyes searching for his mother.

Claire Trent bumped into a young man trying to get away. The man went sprawling on the ground.

She ignored him and carried on running. One of the armed officers had tripped over the pavement and he too went sprawling.

Nobody stopped to help him.

She ran round the top of the road. A white car was driving straight towards her on the pavement. She jumped out of the way.

It raced past just missing her right foot. Inspector Hurd screaming something.

The car didn't stop,

In slow motion, he brought his rifle up and the recoil jerked it back into his shoulder twice.

From the ground, she saw the white car continue in a straight line for twenty yards before veering right and slamming into a lamp-post.

For a second, the lamp-post wobbled then slowly snapped in two, the top half falling across the car and a long, oblong glass shade shattering over its roof.

Silence, and then the puff of the airbags exploding, followed by the loud whoops of an alarm.

On her left, the armed officers inched cautiously forward, their rifles pointing directly at the vehicle. Dave Hardy tried to move forward too but was waved back by the uniformed Inspector.

One of the armed response team ran round to the front of the car, keeping his rifle trained on the windscreen. He shouted, 'All clear' raising his fist to the air.

Claire Trent picked herself up from the floor. Her knee was grazed and her hip bruised. A shoe with a broken heel lay in the gutter. She bent over to pick it up and limped over to the inspector standing in front of the car.

Inside, a young man was sitting upright, his body kept in place by the airbag.

The face was covered in a sort of talcum powder and his forehead was shattered where the officer's bullet had exited. Blood dripped slowly down his cheeks, staining the white powder from the airbag.

Claire Trent looked back up the road.

A body was lying to one side, its leg stretched out at a strange angle.

Charlie Whitworth.

She began limping back to where he lay, shouting, 'Charlie, Charlie!'

## Chapter Seventy-Three

The phone rang and rang. Why wasn't Charlie picking up?

He checked the number to make sure. It was right.

He pressed redial, hearing the ring tone loud and clear. But still no answer. Where was Charlie? In the middle of something and that was why he wasn't picking up?

He couldn't wait any longer. He called Claire Trent. Charlie would be pissed off but sod it, this was too important.

'Yes?' Her voice was loud and clear.

'It's Ridpath, guvnor. I've got the name and address of the man behind all the killings.'

There was a long sigh down the end of the phone. 'His name is Reginald Stokes and he lived at a place called Bridgewater Lane.'

How did she know? 'That's it, guvnor we need...'

'We've already sent an armed team to the address, Ridpath. Mr Stokes is in front of me now. He's dead.'

Ridpath was stunned. A thousand questions raced through his mind. How? What? Why?

Claire Trent carried on speaking. 'He just tried to shoot up Michael Connelly's house but was shot dead by an armed response team.'

Ridpath tried to take it all in. Why would he do that?

Claire Trent continued. 'But I have some bad news. Charlie Whitworth has been injured, badly I'm afraid. It's not looking good... sorry Ridpath, I have to go, somebody is calling me.'

The phone line went dead.

Charlie was injured?

Ridpath sat down on the chair.

Maureen was staring at him. 'What's happened?' she finally asked.

Ridpath didn't answer. He just looked at the grey carpet and then he noticed his hand was shaking and it wouldn't stop.

## Chapter Seventy-Four

It was three hours later when he received the call from Claire Trent to be at her office by five p.m.

What did she want? To give him another bloody reprimand?

He was kept waiting for twenty minutes before he was finally called in. It was like waiting for an audience with the queen. Despite the success of the operation, the office was subdued, Charlie's injuries heavy on everyone's mind.

He knocked on the door, receiving the curt instruction to enter.

'Sit down, Ridpath.'

He took the only chair in front of her desk.

'I've called you in today...'

'Before we start, ma'am, I wonder if I can ask about Charlie. How is he? Nobody knew outside...'

She looked down at her hands on the table. 'It's touch and go. He's in the infirmary. Multiple fractures I was told. In surgery at the moment. We'll know more when he comes out.'

'Thanks for telling me.'

'You two were close?'

'Until recently we were. He hasn't quite forgiven me for the Beast of Manchester case...'

'Charlie has a memory on him.'

'And then some. He once told me to always get my retaliation in first. I thought he was joking until I saw his face.'

'He was old school was DCI Whitworth.' Then her face suddenly reddened and she corrected herself. 'He *is* old school, that's what I meant.'

Ridpath covered her embarrassment by asking a question. 'You wanted to see me?'

She shuffled some papers on her desk. 'I called you in to let you know you were right.'

Ridpath's eyebrows rose.

'We checked with army records. Reginald Stokes was born Reginald Wilson in 1995. He had a twin brother, Ronald. His father was gunned down the same year and his mother married David Stokes in 1996. At sixteen, he went to the Army Foundation College in Aldershot, afterwards joining REME as an armourer and serving two tours of duty in Afghanistan. He left the army nine months ago.'

'When did he come back to Manchester?'

'As far as we can make out, almost immediately. The house is registered under his real father's name, Harry Wilson, but was only bought earlier this year.'

'Where did he get the money?'

She shrugged her shoulders. 'We haven't worked that one out yet. He seems to have blamed Michael Connelly for the death of his father. I've read the case files and Connelly was present in the pub the day it happened...'

'He gave a witness statement to Ted Roylance, the investigating officer.'

It was the turn of Claire Trent to raise her eyebrows. 'How do you know?'

'I read the case file.'

'You have been a busy detective. And here was I thinking you were just a pretty face.' Once again she reddened from the throat upwards. She picked up another sheet of paper. 'A scene of crime team is in the house as we speak. It appears the cellar may have been used to detain people.'

'Perhaps Gerard Connelly and Phil Marsland?'

'Possibly. They are collecting DNA and fingerprint samples from the house and cellars. Let's not jump to any conclusions before we have proof, shall we?'

'Protheroe called me an hour ago.'

'Really? He hasn't seen fit to call me...'

'I said I would tell you. He's writing his report right now. You should get it this evening.'

'And?'

'There are DNA matches to both Gerard Connelly and Ronald Wilson on the rope used to bind Phil Marsland...'

'He used the same rope?

'Apparently. Maybe he didn't think we would tie the three cases together.' It was Ridpath's turn to go red. 'I meant link the three cases together.'

'I know what you meant, Ridpath. But it is interesting, isn't it?'

'What ma'am?'

'If you hadn't been working for the coroner, we would never have made the connection.' She glanced at her computer. 'Shit, is that the time?' She stood up and began collecting her papers together. 'I've an interview on *Granada Reports* at 6:30. It's telly time.'

'Good luck, ma'am.'

'Thanks Ridpath.'

He turned to leave her office.

'And Ridpath...'

'Yes, ma'am.'

'Thanks for all your work. You've done well.'

Ridpath nodded his head.

'But if you ever call me ma'am again, you'll be cleaning out the bogs at Strangeways. Do I make myself clear?'

'As clear as a pint of Boddies... guvnor.'

## Chapter Seventy-Five

It was late when Ridpath arrived home. After the meeting with Claire Trent he had driven back to Stockfield to brief Margaret Challinor.

'An eventful day, Ridpath.'

'You're telling me.'

'Anything more on Detective Chief Inspector Whitworth?'

'I haven't received any messages, but his surgery must be over by now. I guess I'll find out tomorrow.'

'And Claire Trent, how's she handling all this?'

Ridpath had forgotten the two of them knew each other. 'I don't know honestly, I didn't ask. It's not the sort of thing you say to a senior officer. I think she's OK. Seems to be relishing the pressure, if I think about it.'

'A bit of an adrenalin junkie, if you ask me. Bright and tough, but she flies close to the sun, if you understand what I mean.'

Ridpath nodded his head. 'Don't we all. Comes with the territory.'

'Do you think I should postpone the Ronald Wilson inquest on Thursday?' she said, changing the subject.

'It's up to you but I would say don't. The pathologist's report was pretty clear so I think you can deliver a coroner's verdict of murder by a person, or persons unknown. The police will have to reopen their enquiry and come to a new conclusion in their report anyway...'

'Good, I was hoping you would say that. Are there any relatives left alive as far you know?'

Ridpath shook his head. 'I don't think so. There is a daughter but we haven't been able to find her so far.'

'I don't suppose it matters. The State will take care of the funeral in the absence of relatives. I'll open separate inquests on the other victims of Reginald Wilson. I think you said there were three others?'

'The pathologist reports links two others: Gerard Connelly and Phil Marsland. I think he also killed Elsie Granger.'

'Why?'

'She was the only one who could tell us the information we needed about the family. To be honest, without the help of Maureen O'Dowd at Reddish, it would have taken me far longer to work it all out.

'Somebody to assist you makes it all much easier.'

'Tell me about it.'

She stood up. 'Right, I'm going home and so should you.' Her voice dropped a register. 'Can I be straightforward with you, Ridpath?'

He wondered what she was going to say. 'Go ahead.'

'You look terrible. Like you haven't slept for two days.'

Ridpath realised his hair was wet and he was sweating despite her office being quite cold. 'Just tired, Mrs Challinor. A good night's sleep will help.'

'Why don't you come in late tomorrow? Take the morning off.'

Ridpath thought about it. Perhaps he could take Eve and Polly to school again. He'd forgotten how much he enjoyed their mornings together. 'I might take you up on your offer, Mrs Challinor.'

It was eleven when he arrived home that night. He thought about ringing Polly but decided it was too late, she would already be asleep. He would try tomorrow morning before school.

He trudged upstairs, feeling like it was a mountain he was climbing. Taking off his clothes seemed to take ages but finally he was buried deep beneath the duvet.

His body ached, his head hurt and he was sweating like he had just run a bloody marathon, but, as his eyes closed, one thought fought its way up from deep in his subconscious.

*What had happened to Harry Wilson's daughter?*

# Day Eight

*Wednesday, April 25, 2018*

# Chapter Seventy-Six

Ridpath woke covered in sweat. His head was pounding and his mouth was dry. But one thought still echoed around his mind.

*What had happened to Harry Wilson's daughter?*

He glanced down at the time. 9:20 a.m.

Shit. Shit. Shit.

The he remembered his final act before falling asleep last night was to switch off the alarm. He climbed out of bed, feeling his muscles ache and his bones creak.

*Should he go to Christies?*

He had obviously caught a cold. Dr Morris had been direct. If he caught cold or flu, he was to go to the hospital straight away. He would call Mrs Challinor later, she was sure to understand.

He staggered into the bathroom and looked in the mirror. He wasn't the best of sights first thing in the morning. Polly always said he looked like a cross between Rupert Bear and the Honey Monster. He stuck out his tongue, coated in a sticky white fur. His eyes were even worse; red-rimmed and rheumy, like an eighty year old who'd partied all their life.

He should go to Christies. If they kept him in, it didn't matter. Better to be safe than sorry.

His mobile rang in the bedroom. He rushed back and found it charging beside his bed. 'Ridpath' he said, hearing his voice creak.

'Hiya, it's Maureen, from Reddish.'

'Good morning, Maureen.'

'Am I disturbing you?'

Standing there in his boxer shorts in an empty house, she wouldn't be disturbing anything. 'No, Maureen, how can I help you?'

'Well, I've been thinking about Harry Wilson's family...'

'Yes...'

'And we know the twins found homes. One stayed with the mother and went down south, and the other stayed with the grandparents...'

He knew where she was going with this.

'...but what happened to the daughter?'

He shivered. There it was. The same question had been haunting his dreams all night.

'Go on...'

'Well, like I said, I do a bit of family history in my spare time. I found out I'm related to the Pendle witches...'

Why didn't it surprise him? But he answered, 'That's interesting.'

'One day I'll tell you all about it, But staying on Harry Wilson and his daughter, it struck me perhaps there may have been other relatives, so I researched his side of the family.'

'Perhaps the daughter went to the paternal grandparents?'

'You've got it.'

'And?'

'There weren't any. Harry Wilson was an orphan.'

Ridpath sighed, all the breath seemed to rush out of his lungs. She had rung him at this time in the morning to tell him this news?

'But it got me thinking. What if the daughter was adopted?'

'Christine.'

'What?'

'The daughter's name was Christine,' Ridpath repeated.

'And it also struck me Harry Wilson's obituary said he was buried according to the rites of the Holy Mother Church.' He could hear the excitement in Maureen's voice now.

'Her mother, Elsie Granger, kept a crucifix in her hallway. She asked me to bless myself before I left.'

'So I thought if the parents were devout Catholics, what if...?'

'The daughter was adopted through one of the Catholic agencies?'

'Right first time, Ridpath. So I rang Caritas first thing this morning...'

'Caritas?'

'The Catholic Adoption Agency for the Diocese of Salford. For some strange reason, Manchester is in Salford for Catholics. 'Caritas' is based at the cathedral there.'

Ridpath could feel his own excitement rising. 'And?'

'They do have a Christine Wilson in their records adopted in 1997, but they won't release the information.'

'You told them this was a police matter.'

'Of course, but they still wouldn't release the documents. I can understand their point of view; we could be anybody on the phone asking for records. They just can't give them out to anybody.'

'So we need a warrant. It could take a while depending on the judge.'

'Well... no. I explained the urgency of the situation and how it might prevent more murders and they've agreed if we go down there and show our identification, they will release the records.'

'When can we go?'

'Now, if we want.'

'You're a star, Maureen.'

'It did help that the bishop is my godfather. He vouched for me.'

'It helps to know people in high places. Give me thirty minutes. Where will I meet you?'

'Outside the cathedral on the Close.'

'See you at ten o'clock.'

He put the phone down. This case was finally slotting into place. The woman was the key. It was she who had rung the police to report Ronald Wilson's supposed suicide. It was she who had been seen on the CCTV with Gerard Connelly before he disappeared. And Phil Marsland had been going on a date with an unknown woman when he vanished.

She was the key to everything and she was still out there, Ridpath knew it.

# Chapter Seventy-Seven

They met at Cathedral Close just off Chapel Street in Salford. Ridpath arrived first and stood in front of the solid, imposing cathedral.

He remembered his mum's family had grown up in this area in the twenties. She had often described the tenements, back-to-back houses, pubs on every corner and the 'characters' of the area like L. S. Lowry, Jimmy Hewitt and Walter Greenwood. 'Just read *Love on the Dole* if you want to know what it was like. Policemen used to walk around in threes.'

It had changed now. All the old houses were knocked down, the shops demolished, and the sense of community was completely destroyed.

The area was going through what was known as 'urban renewal' which involved levelling everything and leaving it empty until property developers decided it was ripe for gentrification.

Since the opening of Media City down the road, that point had now been reached. Everywhere in front of him, roads were being widened, acres of waste ground were being filled with new apartments and the derelict pubs refurbished into lifestyle cafes or, even worse, gastropubs.

Luckily, Maureen arrived to rescue him from the sight of a destroyed Salford.

'Hiya, been waiting long?'

'Long enough to hate this.'

'Aye, I know what you mean. Only the cathedral has survived. Shall we go inside, Vera is waiting for us.'

Vera was warm and typically northern; honest, down-to-earth and friendly. 'Are you Detective Inspector Ridpath? Nice to meet you. I believe you want to look at an adoptee's records?'

'That's correct. Here are the details of the person we're looking for, Christine Wilson. She would now be aged twenty-five and was probably adopted in 1996 or 1997. She's suspected of being involved in multiple murders.'

Vera's hand came to her mouth. 'Normally, we only release records to the adoptee or a next of kin.'

'I understand, but as you know, this case is extremely urgent. At the moment, I am acting on behalf of the East Manchester coroner. We could subpoena the records, but time is of the essence if we are to prevent further murders.'

'I have been instructed by the bishop to provide you with assistance. We have a duty of care to the adoptees and to their records. Before I show you the documents, I'll need proof of identity, and also from you, Maureen.'

Ridpath handed over his warrant card, followed by Maureen giving her identity card and her designation card.

'You're lucky there's no veto on the records.'

'Veto?' asked Ridpath.

'Some adoptees do not want to be contacted. They may not be ready to meet their birth mother or relatives, or have simply moved on, leaving the past behind. Either way, if there were a veto in place, I wouldn't be able to release anything.'

'I understand.'

She placed a brown envelope on the desk. 'I printed them out after receiving Maureen's call this morning. She was originally placed in St Michael's before being adopted. I'm afraid the records are patchy, so I would like to manage your expectations. The nuns at the time were overworked and sometimes they were not as diligent as they should have been.'

'Not a problem, I just need the name and address of the adopting family.'

'I'll leave you to open them together.'

She stood up and went into a back room.

Ridpath took a deep breath. 'Well, here goes.' He slid his finger under the sealed flap and pulled out four sheets of paper. The first was a photocopy of an admission form to St Michael's Home, giving her name, age, and her parent's name.

Maureen was looking over his shoulder. 'See,' she pointed to a handwritten note from a Sister Hermione. 'The child's mother has since remarried and moved away from Manchester. She has requested the child be adopted by a Catholic family,' she read out loud.

The second sheet was the formal release for adoption form signed by Doreen Wilson and dated October 1996.

'Not long after she married again.' Maureen's face was closer now, almost perched on his shoulder.

The third sheet was a record written by the sisters. During her stay at St Michael's. Alongside a variety of dates during 1996 and 1997 were words like Wilful. Stubborn. Punished for disobedience. Refused to eat. Temper tantrums. Spitting. Fighting.

'She obviously didn't like the nuns,' said Maureen

'I don't blame her. Why would you ever give children into the care of a group of women who have sworn they will never have children? It has never made sense to me.'

Maureen was about to answer when he turned to the fourth page. The title said 'Notice of Adoption'. After the usual legal language, the name and address of the adopting couple appeared half way down.

'Jesus Christ,' said Ridpath out loud.

The volunteer workers in the centre stopped what they were doing, and all turned to stare at him.

# Chapter Seventy-Eight

'It's very unusual, Ridpath.'

'But can you do it, Mrs Challinor?'

She shrugged her elegant shoulders. 'I have the power, but…'

'Why don't I just send a team to arrest her?'

Claire Trent had joined them after being asked by the coroner. Outside, the sun was going down on a Manchester spring day and the street lights were just coming on.

Ridpath ran his fingers through his thinning hair. He felt better than he did this morning, but hot and cold flushes still swept through his body. His one mantra was to keep going until tomorrow and then he would check himself into Christies, letting the doctors do their worst.

'Well, Ridpath…?'

'Because we don't have any proof, guvnor. It's all circumstantial at the moment.' Ridpath had taken both of them through the documents he had found this morning and the research he had carried out with Maureen O'Dowd.

'The SOC team are going through the house, they're bound to find evidence that she was there.'

'It was owned by her father. She could just say she visited in the past and we'd be stuffed. There are no trace elements on any of the bodies other than that of Reggie Wilson.'

Claire Trent slowly shook her head. 'I'm still not sure…'

'I'm inclined to think Ridpath is right. Tomorrow is our only chance of stopping her once and for all. If she's allowed to go free, she may want to carry on with her vendetta.'

Claire Trent interjected quickly. We can't have any more trouble. Despite the death of Reginald Wilson, Manchester is on the point of exploding. Michael Connelly still thinks Big Terry was behind it all. While the rest of the gangs are trying to arm themselves. We had reports earlier from confidential informants of even more guns arriving from London and Liverpool. And last night, a firebomb was thrown through the window of the Wheatsheaf.'

'Big Terry's pub?'

Claire Trent nodded.

'It's a tinder keg waiting for a spark…'

'Unless, we can defuse it,' said Mrs Challinor. 'I believe Ridpath's plan is the only way.'

'Have the subpoenas already gone out?'

'Jenny…' shouted the coroner.

The door was already being opened. The office manager stood in the doorway wearing a bright gingham outfit with even brighter pink lipstick. 'Yes, coroner.'

'Have the…?'

'Yes, coroner, as you requested. And all have been delivered.'

'Thank you.' The door closed. 'As you can see, Claire, we've already set the wheels in motion. Your men will go to work tomorrow morning. We start the inquest at 9:30. I'll swear in the jury at nine a.m.'

'My men are ready. I'm still not…'

'Good,' the coroner interrupted. 'We are set. And don't worry, I will take full responsibility if it goes pear-shaped. My reputation with the chief coroner is already shot. One more stick of wood for him to throw on my funeral pyre doesn't matter.' She closed her notebook. 'Now, if you'll both excuse me, I need time to prepare. I'm going to be working late.'

# Day Nine

*Thursday, April 26, 2018*

# Chapter Seventy-Nine

The following morning Ridpath stood outside Stockfield Coroner's Court feeling like death warmed up.

He hadn't slept well. He was either too hot or too cold all night. For hours he had lain in the dark thinking about the case, pulling on or kicking off the duvet.

Had he made any mistakes?

Was the research correct?

Could he be wrong?

Was she really the woman who made the phone call to the police about Ronald Wilson's suicide?

Was she the woman in the CCTV picture with Gerard Connelly?

His mind turned over each fact again and again and again until finally he finally drifted off, only to wake up shivering at five a.m. with the sheets soaked.

After court he would check himself into Christies. He just had to keep going for a couple of more hours.

He had tried to ring Polly in the evening, leaving a message on her answering machine. She hadn't called him back yet, but that wasn't surprising. The mornings were hectic enough anyway, with both her and Eve being perpetually late for school. He was sure she would return his call at lunchtime, when she had a second.

Tommy Harper was the first to arrive, the Uber dropping him outside the court. He looked almost professional in a new suit, crisp white shirt and tie.

'Are you ready, Tommy.'

'Aye, done me homework.' He held up the notes Ridpath had prepared for him the night before.

'Don't worry, you'll be great.'

A police Transit van stopped right opposite them. Michael Connelly stepped out, shrugging off the arm of one of the biggest police officers Ridpath had ever seen. Following him were Graham Connelly and the daughter, Carmela. She must have been released from hospital already.

'Is this a guard of honour, Ridpath,' asked Michael Connelly.

'No red carpet, I'm afraid.'

'You forgot it? What a shame. Another screw up and they'll have you looking after lost property.'

Ridpath ignored him, talking directly to the larger of the policeman. 'Any problems?'

He shook his head. 'All three of them were ready and waiting.'

'Why are we here?' demanded Graham Connelly as belligerent as ever.

'Because you have been subpoenaed to attend by the coroner.'

'Is this about Gerard?' Michael's voice was softer. 'You said there would be an inquest.'

'Gerard's inquest will be later, but today's events do have a bearing on his death.'

As Ridpath was speaking another Transit van parked behind the first.

'What's that bastard doing here?' shouted Michael Connelly, before being restrained by two coppers.

Big Terry was walking nonchalantly down from the van. He turned to his daughter behind him. 'Look what shit's turned up, Tracy.'

Before Ridpath could react, the two of them were in each other's faces, shouting and screaming, joined by their respective families, the two daughters in the thick of the action. It took eight burly coppers to separate the warring factions.

'Take the Connellys up the stairs first and make sure you keep them apart.'

'I'm gonna kill you, Connelly,' Tracy shouted as they were being led to the courtroom.

'You're gonna keep your mouth shut,' said Ridpath, feeling his voice begin to break and his throat ache with the strain of speaking.

'Don't you talk to my daughter like that.'

'Get them out of my sight before I charge them with obstruction,' shouted Ridpath, hearing his voice break.

The uniforms led them upstairs, struggling and shouting all the way.

A large black car had already arrived. Claire Trent was stepping out of the car, followed by the two newest members of the MIT team, Lorraine Caruso and Catherine Delaney.

'Is Margaret ready, Ridpath?'

'As ready as she ever will be, guvnor.'

'That's not an answer that fills me with confidence.'

'How's Charlie?'

Claire Trent shook her head. 'Still in intensive care in an induced coma. Multiple fractures of the ribs and a fractured leg, but that's not the worst. Apparently they found bleeding in the brain. They've released the pressure so all we can do now is hope and pray for the best.'

Ridpath didn't know what to say. He never did in these situations, even with people he knew, despite having received hours of training. 'How's the wife and family handling it?'

'Not well. The wife spent the night beside his bed. But there's nothing she can do except wait and see.' She looked at her watch. 'Should we go up?'

'The coroner should be ready to start by now. Connelly and Big Terry are already up there.'

Claire Trent started up the stairs followed by the two female detectives. She stopped after three steps. 'Is this going to work, Ridpath?'

'I hope so, guvnor. I bloody hope so.'

# Chapter Eighty

Ridpath took one last look at the streets of Stockfield. Office workers were carrying their coffee to work. A man was walking a dog, following it everywhere with a pink plastic bag. An old woman, scarf tied over her head, inched slowly along the road dragging an ageing shopping trolley behind her.

He couldn't postpone it any longer. He turned and slowly climbed the stairs, his fingers crossed behind his back.

As he pushed through the door Mrs Challinor walked in at the front of the court and sat behind her raised desk. He expected some fanfare, as in the High Court, but there was nothing. She simply opened her files and began speaking.

Her tone was relaxed and informal. 'Today we open the inquest into the death of Ronald George Wilson which was postponed from last Thursday, April 20. There will be a jury present at this inquest. They have already been sworn by one of my officers.'

Ridpath glanced across at the jury. Seven men and women, all looking fairly prosperous, sat in a box on the right. Mounted above them a large television screen was ready to display exhibits and run any footage of film that needed to be shown.

Mrs Challinor carried on speaking. 'Representing the police we have Ms Marjorie Salmon.'

The barrister stood up and bowed her head once.

'As there are no living relatives of the deceased as far as we are aware, there are no family members present. Nonetheless, the family's interests will be represented by this court. It is my duty to see that the death of their son is explained and understood.' She paused for a second, 'Ms Oates...'

The senior coroner stepped forward. Ridpath could see her blonde hair was decorated in an elaborate bun, and her suit was a severe black.

'Please call the first witness.'

Tommy Harper strode to the witness box and took the oath on a bible held by Carol Oates. As Margaret Challinor began questioning him, he sat back and answered clearly just as Ridpath had coached him.

'Please state your name and occupation.'

'Detective Sergeant Thomas Harper, at present attached to J Division of GMP, based at Reddish police station.'

'Good morning, detective sergeant, you were in charge of the investigation into the death of Ronald Wilson whose body was found at Wingate Park on the 12th of April 2018. Is that correct?'

'That is correct, coroner. The body was discovered floating there by a group of children. The lake is also known as the Secret Lake by locals.'

'How do you think it got that name, detective?'

'I'm not certain, ma'am, but it's hidden from view behind factories and is not the easiest place to find. It took me a while to find it myself...'

Tommy was doing well; confident firm delivery with a voice suggesting calm professionalism. The hours spent coaching him last night were paying off.

Mrs Challinor continued to explore the details of the discovery of the body. It was when she got to the most important point that Ridpath listened closely.

'Are you sure a woman rang your station to tell them a man was taking off his clothes and entering the water?'

'Positive ma'am. I have taken the liberty of bringing a tape recording of the phone call, recorded at the station on the day in question.'

Jenny came forward and took the MP3 file from Tommy Harper. She placed it in the playback machine. Instantly, the conversation was heard through the speakers on the television screens.

'Reddish police station, how can I help you?' Maureen's voice filled the Coroner's Court.

'I saw the posters you put around town.' It was a woman's voice.

'Which posters, madam?'

'The ones where you were asking about that man, Ronald Wilson.'

'Oh yes, and what do you have to report?'

'I saw somebody like that going for a swim in the Secret Lake.'

'Sorry, can you repeat that?'

'I saw somebody who matched that description take off his clothes and go swimming in the Secret Lake. You know, the one behind the recycling plant.'

'I know where you mean, madam. It's also called Wingate Lake. You say he took off his clothes and went swimming?'

'That's right, he laid his wallet on top of the clothes and just walked into the lake wearing nothing but his boxer shorts.'

'When was this?'

'Last week.'

'But when exactly?'

'Look, I've got to go now.'

'If I could just take your name and address, madam...'

But the courtroom was filled with the sound of a disconnected line. Mrs Challinor carried on her interrogation of Tommy Harper as the noise ceased. 'This was the call you received.'

'It was. But subsequently the post-mortem revealed the call to be false. Ronald Wilson could not have walked into the lake because he was already dead,'

'Yes, thank you, detective, we will be calling the pathologist to tell us about his findings. You are excused.'

Ridpath noticed she didn't ask Tommy why he hadn't followed up on the report. If he had, the body would have been found sooner.

'I would like Dr John Schofield to take the stand.'

He hadn't noticed the doctor before. He was sitting in the corner furthest away from Ridpath. The detective took the opportunity to cough and clear his throat. He was feeling hot now, his forehead burning up. He would grab a cab to Christies when this was finished, the sooner the better.

The two crime families were sitting at the back of the court, surrounded by uniformed policemen. Big Terry was studiously cleaning his fingernails while Michael Connelly was staring into space, as if bored by the whole proceedings. Only Graham Connelly looked interested at what was going on.

After Dr Schofield had finished the formalities, Mrs Challinor began questioning him.

'You were called to a body found in Wingate Lake on April 12th, 2018?'

'That is correct, the body was of a young male aged approximately twenty-three years old.'

'And what did you discover, doctor?'

'I initially thought this was a tragic death by drowning, probably due to excess alcohol or drug consumption. But during the post-mortem I found some disturbing evidence.'

'Which was?'

'There were none of the usual signs of fresh water drowning, particularly no water in the lungs.'

'Why is the absence of water in the lungs important?'

'Because it meant that Ronald Wilson was already dead when he entered the water.'

'Are you sure, doctor? This evidence is key to my final submission to the jury.'

'Absolutely positive. My conclusion that he was already dead when the body was placed in the water was confirmed when I

337

found a small hole in the back of his skull behind the right ear. On opening the skull, I found the injury had penetrated into the brain to a depth of five inches, causing death.'

'Let me get this clear, doctor. Ronald George Wilson was stabbed through the head?'

'Yes, coroner, by a sharp, thin instrument such as an awl or a knitting needle.'

'He was already dead when he was placed in the water?'

'Correct, coroner.'

'So, what do you think of the tape we have just heard where a woman rang the police saying she had seen Ronald Wilson take off his clothes and enter the water.'

'I can't think anything of the tape. But I can tell you that according to my scientific investigation, it would have been impossible for Ronald Wilson to enter the water of his own accord. To put it bluntly, dead men can't walk into water.'

'Thank you, doctor, that's all for now.'

A buzz was going round the court. Both the Connellys and the Marslands were actually listening to the testimony. Graham Connelly was even taking notes, perhaps trying to learn something for his next appearance in court. Claire Trent and her detectives were sitting forward in their seats.

From where he was standing Ridpath could see it all. He coughed twice to clear his throat and suddenly felt very like he wanted to throw up. But he controlled himself, swallowing down hard on his sore throat. He couldn't miss what was going to happen next.

He crossed his fingers as Mrs Challinor spoke in a loud, firm voice to the entire court.

## Chapter Eighty-One

'I now call Carmela Connelly to the witness stand.'

There was a collective look of surprise on the faces of the Connellys, followed by a loud 'What?' from Michael Connelly.

'I call Carmela Connelly,' Mrs Challinor repeated.

Carmela pointed to her chest, looking around at her father and brother on either side. 'You want me?' she finally asked.

'You are Carmela Connelly?' said Mrs Challinor.

Carol Oates had moved silently to stand beside the young woman.

'I am.'

'Then I would like you to take the witness stand.'

Michael Connelly finally recovered from his shock. 'Why do you want to question my daughter? She doesn't even know Ronnie Wilson or whatever his name was?' The old man stood up and was immediately pulled back into his seat by the policeman sitting next to him. The other copper had his hand on Graham Connelly's shoulder.

As Carmela was being led to the witness stand by Carol Oates, she glanced briefly back at her father, mouthing 'help me'.

He tried to get up but was immediately restrained by the police. 'You can't do this. That's my daughter. I'm gonna kill youse bastards...'

'Mr Connelly, if you don't be quiet, I will hold you in contempt. Police officers, please ensure Mr Connelly doesn't disturb these proceedings.'

Two more policemen went to sit behind Michael and Graham Connelly.

Carol Oates held up a bible. 'Do you want to take the oath, or will you affirm that you will tell the truth and nothing but the truth.'

Carmela Connelly had recovered her composure by now. 'I ain't swearing nothing.'

'It is a legal requirement that you need to swear an oath before giving evidence.'

'I told you, you dozy cow, I ain't swearing nothing.'

Carol Oates glanced across at the coroner who nodded her head slightly.

'We will assume the witness has affirmed. Your name is Carmela Connelly, is that correct?'

'Why you asking? You just called my name, why you asking again? You forgot already?'

Michael Connelly stopped struggling with the policemen and listened to his daughter.

Mrs Challinor continued. 'And your birthday is November 15th, 1993?'

'You gonna send me a card, are you?'

'I'll ask again. Your birthday is November 15th, 1993?'

'Yeah, what of it? A lady doesn't reveal her age, does she? How old are you?'

'I ask the questions in this court, Ms Connelly.'

'Well, why don't you get on with it? I'm wasting my time here...'

Mrs Challinor coughed loudly. 'I have only one question for you today...'

'Well, ask it will ya, I ain't got all day.'

Graham Connelly laughed out loud. His father was beaming from ear to ear. A proud dad.

'As I said, I have just one question,' repeated Mrs Challinor.

'You said that already.'

Graham Connelly laughed again, louder this time. 'You tell 'em sis. Don't take no bollocks from this mob.'

Mrs Challinor stared at the young man before continuing. 'The question is simple. 'Why did you kill your brother?'

## Chapter Eighty-Two

The court erupted.

The Connellys were shouting and swearing as the police desperately tried to restrain them. Big Terry and his family were on their feet. Claire Trent and her detectives were trying to get everybody to sit down. Mrs Challinor was banging on her desk with a tiny hammer shouting, 'Order, order!'

Ridpath felt faint. His forehead was hot and his mouth was dry, yet his shirt was drenched with sweat beneath his jacket. The noise washed over him and he stayed where he was leaning against the door as the police fought to bring the court under control. He felt he should help them but found his feet unable to move.

Eventually, after two minutes, order was restored and everybody, including the Connellys, were forced back to their seats.

'I will not have such outbursts in my court again. Anybody who disturbs this coroner in the course of her work will be charged with contempt of court and immediately taken to a cell, do I make myself clear? She turned to face Carmela Connelly. 'I will ask you again. Why did you kill your brother?'

A smile slowly spread across her face. 'I don't know what you mean? My brother Gerard was run over on the M60 by a lorry.'

'In this case, I meant, your real brother, Ronald Wilson.'

Once again the court erupted in shouting as the Connellys and Big Terry's family rose, raising their voices. It took all the assembled police plus constant shouts from Mrs Challinor to regain control.

'This is the last time I will put up with such disgraceful behaviour in my court. The next person who raises his voice will be charged under the Contempt of Court Act 1981 and face imprisonment of up to one month. Do I make myself clear?' Her staring eyes fixed on Michael Connelly and Big Terry Marsland until both looked down at the floor. She turned to the jury. 'Members of the jury, you will ignore the interruption and focus on the questions and answers of the witnesses. Now, Ms Connelly, I will ask you for a third time. Why did you kill your brother Ronald Wilson?'

The court was silent now. Only a slight buzz from the speakers in the televisions broke the quiet. Ridpath focused all his attention on the young woman, waiting for her to answer.

Finally, she spoke in a soft, hesitant voice. 'I don't know what you mean.'

Mrs Challinor handed a piece of paper to Carol Oates. 'You have told us your birth date is November 15th, 1993…'

'Yeah, what of it?'

'On the screen you will see the birth certificate of Christine Wilson, born on the same day in the same year as you.'

A green and cream sheet of paper appeared on the television screens in the court. The names of the parents, Harry Wilson and Doreen Wilson nee Granger were written in flowing black script as was the name of their daughter, Christine.

'So?' Carmela Connelly answered. 'She has the same birth date as I do, so what?'

Mrs Challinor's voice softened. 'This is you, Christine, isn't it?'

'Why are you calling me Christine? My name is Carmela.'

The birth certificate was replaced with another two more birth certificates, one above the other.

Mrs Challinor continued speaking. 'Two years afterwards, Christine, the twins Ronald and Reginald were born to your parents, Harry and Doreen.'

'I've told you my name is Carmela.'

'Unfortunately, your father was murdered in 1996.' Two more pictures appeared on the screen. A close up of a smiling face taken from a mug shot and a crime scene picture of a man lying on the floor of a pub, blood flowing out of a gaping wound in the back of his head.

The young woman didn't say a word, simply staring at the screen above her head.

Mrs Challinor's voice continued speaking, soft and reassuring in tone. 'The next year or so wasn't a good time for you, Christine, you were placed in St Michael's Home, an orphanage run by the Sisters of Mercy, even though your mother was still alive.'

The report on Christine Wilson from the nuns appeared on the screen. The words in bold stood out against the fading paper. **Wilful. Stubborn. Punished for disobedience. Refused to eat. Temper tantrums. Spitting. Fighting.**

The young woman stared at her hands gripping the wooden rail. Her voice when it spoke was like that of a child. 'She didn't want me. My own mother didn't want me.'

'Did you see her again? asked Mrs Challinor gently.

'Just the once. She came to see me in the summer when I was in the orphanage. I was so happy to see her again. I tried to kiss her but she wouldn't let me. I begged and pleaded with her to take me out of there, but she said she was getting married again and she was taking Reggie with her to the south. She left me there all alone with those hateful nuns. Left me...' her voice trailed off.

The court was quiet, everybody staring at the young woman in the witness chair.

A new image appeared on the screen.

'This is your adoption certificate, Christine. Could you read out the names of the adopting couple, please?'

Nobody in the court moved. Michael Connelly and Big Terry were both staring at the screen.'

The young woman slowly lifted her head, focusing on the screen. 'It says… Christine Wilson was adopted by the Michael and Carmen Connelly on October 6th, 1997.'

'We loved you, Carmela,' said Michael Connelly.

'But I didn't love you. And neither did Carmen.' The young woman swivelled her head round to face Michael Connelly, her green eyes filled with anger. 'She told me everything before she died. 'About you, about Harry Wilson. She was having an affair with him. But you knew that. didn't you? That's why you had him killed. That's why you had my father killed.'

'I didn't, I didn't.'

'Everybody thought it was just business, you wanting to be in control. But it wasn't, was it? It was jealousy. You were jealous of my father.

'I loved you, Carmela.'

'MY NAME IS CHRISTINE,' she shouted. 'Carmen hated you. Hated every ounce and every inch of you. She filled me up with hate, and added just a little more, only for me.

'Don't say such things, not now.'

'That's why I kidnapped Gerard, your favourite. I was going to kill him, but he escaped before I could slit his throat. A lorry got him instead. A shame. I so wanted to hear him beg for his life.'

Graham Connelly sat on his chair in the court with his mouth open wide. Next to him, his father covered his ears with his hands.

'But why kill Ronald Wilson?' It was Mrs Challinor asking the question.

The young woman laughed unpleasantly. 'Because he was weak. That old witch had got in his head with all her Catholic rubbish. He needed to die. He deserved to die.'

A plaintive, 'What? What are you saying, Carmela?' came from Michael Connelly.

'Shut up, you old fool. My name's Christine, Christine Wilson.' She pointed directly at him, her face twisted like an angry small child. 'You murdered my father.'

'What?'

'You killed Harry Wilson.' Her voice coiled like a vicious snake.

'I didn't...I...I...' Michael Connelly stammered.

Mrs Challinor leant forward across her desk. 'And Philip Marsland?'

The young woman shrugged her shoulders. 'It was part of the plan. Once these stupid men had stopped killing each other, I was going to take over with Reggie. Nobody could have stopped us. His death was just business.'

'Bitch.' Big Terry stood up and lunged at the young woman, only to be held back by the arms of the police surrounding him.

'And you can shut up too, Marsland, otherwise I'll cut your dick off like I did with your stupid son.'

Her face was vicious now, like a cornered wildcat lashing out with sharp claws at anything that came close.

Claire Trent and her detectives were standing beside the witness box. Calmly and deliberately, she said, 'Christine Wilson, you are under arrest on suspicion of murder. You do not have to say anything, but it may harm your defence if you do not mention when questioned something which you later rely on in court. Anything you do say may be given in evidence.'

These were the last words Ridpath heard as his legs suddenly gave way and the floor of the court rushed up to meet him.

His world went black.

*Two Days Later*

## Chapter Eighty-Three

Ridpath had woken up surrounded by bright light.

His first thought was that this is what death felt like. He had been wrong all these years. God does exist. The atheists are going to be terribly disappointed.

Then he heard a broad Irish accent, County Cork he would have guessed.

'Welcome to the world of the living, Mr Ridpath. It was touch and go for a while there.'

He felt somebody adjusting something above his head.

'There you go Another bottle of saline. We have to keep you hydrated.'

He blinked his eyes three times and a round Irish face slowly swam into focus.

'The doctor will be along in a minute to check you out, but you look better than you did when you arrived, and you'll need no doctor to tell you that.'

She walked away and he closed his eyes. Later, he didn't know how long later, he opened them again to find Dr Morris standing over him.

'Hello there, Mr Ridpath. How do you feel?'

'Like I've just gone three rounds with Mike Tyson,' he managed to croak.

'That's because you came in with pneumonia and it wasn't helped by a rather large bump on your head from falling when you fainted. Luckily, the office manager knew enough about your illness to call us immediately and we whisked you straight in. We've pumped you full of antibiotics and your case was

348

relatively mild. But you've been a very lucky man, Mr Ridpath, a very lucky man indeed.'

'What time is it?'

The doctor checked his watch. '12:30 p.m. on Saturday, April 29th.'

'But... but... it was Thursday...'

'You've been under sedation. It's been the best way to help your body fight the infection and recover your strength. And you've been an incredibly stupid man, if you don't mind me saying so.'

'Has my wife been here?'

'For the last two nights. I think she's as exhausted as you are.' He glanced towards the door of the ward. 'Looks like you have visitors. You're the last patient on my morning list. With a bit of luck, I'll make it to the match on time.'

'United or City?'

'Don't be silly, the best team in the world. Macclesfield Town. Racing up League Two we are.'

Claire Trent and Margaret Challinor walked into Ridpath's field of vision. One was carrying a box of chocolates and the other a bottle of wine.

'Don't stay too long, ladies, he's still a little weak. I'll be seeing you on Monday, Mr Ridpath. Till then, stay hydrated and do everything the nurses tell you. The time for stupidity is over. Understand?'

He walked away leaving the two women standing there.

'Morning, Ridpath, how are you feeling?'

'Like road kill if you must know, Mrs Challinor.'

She placed the chocolates on the bedside table. 'You need to look after yourself better, Ridpath.'

Now she tells me, he thought. Then he remembered the case and his fall from grace. 'Christine Wilson, she...?'

'She's in custody. I charged her yesterday.' Claire Trent presented the wine directly to Ridpath. He didn't know where to put it, so just cradled it in his arms like a baby. 'Her DNA

349

was all over the house near Sale Water Park. Plus we found it in Elsie Granger's house. We think she and her brother killed the old woman.'

'Why?'

'According to her, it was to cover their tracks. The old woman was the only person who knew about her and her brother.'

'But…?'

'But there may be more…'

Margaret Challinor carried on. 'We think she was getting revenge on Elsie Granger for abandoning her as a child, for not wanting her. The death was too vicious, too personal. There are easier ways to kill a person other than slitting their throat.'

'There was always a personal element in all these deaths.'

'She was evil, Ridpath, and through your work we managed to catch her.' Margaret Challinor sat on the only chair close to his bed. Claire Trent remained standing.

'Maureen O'Dowd did most of the work, I just pointed her in the right direction.'

Margaret Challinor leant forward and touched his hand. 'But you can't continue like this, Ridpath, at the moment. Your health won't stand it.'

'But I want to carry on working, Mrs Challinor, I don't want to give up. I'm only thirty-seven for God's sake.'

She glanced at Claire Trent before carrying on speaking. 'That's why I've been in discussions with Detective Superintendent Trent. We both believe you fulfil an important function between the work of the police and of the coroner's office…'

Claire Trent interrupted. 'Frankly, MIT would never have made the connection between the deaths of Ronald Wilson and Gerard Connelly. When you're better, and we hope that's soon, we both want you to continue in your new role for at least the next six months…'

'…We'll see how it goes, but we feel that it's an effective use of resources,' added Mrs Challinor.

'Nice to know I'm a "resource".'

'You know I don't mean it like that. Quite simply, you're effective, Ridpath. Neither of us have worked out how yet, but you are...'

'... We both know it can't go on like this, you're not the sort of person who does things, half-heartedly...' added Claire Trent.

'...So I've found the money to get an assistant coroner's officer for you. Take away some of the workload.'

They were tag-teaming him and he was quite enjoying it.

'What do you think, Ridpath?'

Before he answered, a shadow appeared behind their heads.

'I see you got here before me.'

Polly's voice. His wife and daughter were here to see him.

'Hello, Mrs Ridpath, my name's Claire Trent.' She stuck out her hand which Polly ignored.

'If you ladies don't mind, I'd like to speak to my husband in private.'

Margaret Challinor rose from her chair. 'Of course, we're terribly sorry for intruding.'

As they were both leaving, Ridpath remembered something that was bothering him. 'How's Charlie? I forgot to ask.'

Claire Trent smiled. 'He's out of the coma and it looks like there's no permanent damage. In fact, the first thing he did was demand his cigarettes.'

'He'll be returning to MIT?'

'When he's ready,' she smiled again. 'Think about what we said, Ridpath,' she added as she took Mrs Challinor's arm and both left.

'What did the Wicked Witches of East Manchester want?' Polly said watching them depart. 'Talking about work, I suppose.'

Ridpath didn't answer. 'Where's Eve?' he asked instead.

'She's with my mother. I wanted to have a chat with you.'

*That* sounded ominous.

She sat down on the chair vacated by Mrs Challinor and took his hand. 'You know I love you, Ridpath. I don't know why You are the world's most stupid, arrogant, insufferable, pig-headed man, but for some obscure reason, I love you.'

'I love you too, Poll, always have, always will.'

'Yuen Fen, my mum calls it. Fate. We were destined to meet and be together.'

'I'll buy that, even if it is coming from the Dragon Lady.'

She looked down and patted his hand. 'But… we can't go on like this.'

'I…'

'Let me finish, Ridpath. This is difficult enough for me to say already.' She took a deep breath. 'We can't go on like this. I can't be dreading every time the phone rings just in case some voice on the other end tells me you've collapsed at work and have been taken to Christies…'

'I…'

She held up her hand and he stopped speaking. 'It's not fair on me. It's not fair on Eve. She needs a dad, she doesn't need someone to save the world. She just needs somebody to tuck her in at night, give her hugs, drive her to BTS concerts and criticise her taste in boyfriends. What she definitely doesn't need is to visit a gravestone on a Sunday carrying flowers.'

'It won't come to that, Poll.'

'Won't it? Look where you are, Ridpath. It's not bloody Disneyland, it's a cancer hospital and you're recovering from pneumonia!'

'Look, Poll…'

'Ridpath, it's me and Eve or the job. Which are you going to put first?'

'Poll, it's not like that, I…'

'What's your answer, Ridpath?'

# DI Ridpath Crime Thriller Series

*Where The Truth Lies*
*Where The Dead Fall*